A BIBLIOGRAPHY OF ROBERT WATT, M.D.

AUTHOR OF THE BIBLIOTHECA BRITANNICA

Rob. Watt M. D.

A BIBLIOGRAPHY OF ROBERT WATT, M.D.

AUTHOR OF THE BIBLIOTHECA BRITANNICA

With a Facsimile Edition of His Catalogue of Medical
Books and with a Preliminary Essay on His Works
A Contribution to Eighteenth Century Medical History

By

FRANCESCO CORDASCO

☐

Facti est immensi copia Mundi,
Ovid

Detroit
Gale Research Company
1968

Library of Congress Catalog Card

Number 68-29119

For

DR. ARCHIBALD L. GOODALL,

The Royal Faculty of Physicians and Surgeons, Glasgow
who made this work possible.

PREFACE

In my early student days, in the search for bibliographical literature, I came to know and respect Robert Watt. His *Bibliotheca Britannica* proved an unending source of information. I stood in awe of this vast compendium of titles, and in its continued use, I lamented that Robert Watt was so little known and respected, and that his other work, bibliographical, philosophical and medical, was not generally available. One work of Watt, *The Catalogue of Medical Books,* particularly intrigued me. Finlayson, long ago, in his brief memoir of Watt, had failed to find a copy. Tedder's life of Watt in *The Dictionary of National Biography* noted that the book was especially rare; and elsewhere, when mention of *The Catalogue of Medical Books* was made, the disconsolate observation followed that the book must be considered lost to the world. The historical and bibliographical importance of *The Catalogue* was manifest. I determined to procure a copy. Little did I realise that my determination would entail enquiry at most of the great libraries of the world, and that for many years I was to remain disappointed. My ultimate success amply repays my labour, and the true reward lies in the reaffirmation of Robert Watt's reputation that this edition of his *Catalogue of Medical Books* will make.

To the facsimile edition of *The Catalogue* I have affixed an essay on the works of Watt and a bibliography. As a frontispiece I have reproduced a portrait of Watt which hangs in the Hall of The Faculty of Physicians and Surgeons of Glasgow.

I have incurred many obligations in the search for *The Catalogue.* I am in debt, veritably, to every medical librarian of Western Europe and America. Everywhere I received hope and considerate suggestion. To Dr. W.

B. McDaniel, II, of the College of Physicians of Philadelphia; to Dr. Henry R. Viets of the Boston Medical
Library; to Dr. W. J. Bishop of the London. Wellcome
Historical Medical Library I express my earnest grati-
tude for encouragement and direction. My sister,
Angela Cordasco, gave particular assistance with her
discussions of Edinburgh and Scottish medical history.

The generosity of Dr. Archibald L. Goodall, of The
Royal Faculty of Physicians and Surgeons of Glasgow,
made this work possible, and it is to him that I have
dedicated this memorial to the reputation of his country-
man, Robert Watt.

The recognition of the volume's importance is a testi-
mony to the bibliographical knowledge of its publisher,
William F. Kelleher.

F. C.
May, 1950

NOTE

This volume originally appeared in 1950 and very
quickly went out of print. Repeated requests for copies
have suggested this second edition. In the intervening
years since its publication, the great *Bibliotheca Britannica*
has been republished in an offset edition (New York, Burt
Franklin, 1965). See review by F. Cordasco, "British
Bibliographical Monument: Robert Watt's *Bibliotheca
Britannica*," *Library Journal*, vol. 90 (Sept. 15, 1965) pp.
3584-3585.

F. C.
January, 1968

INTRODUCTION

THE WORKS OF ROBERT WATT (1774-1819)

In the short span of forty-five years of life the Scots-
man, Robert Watt, managed to produce the most monumental bibliographical catalogue ever singly planned
and achieved. His fame lives by virtue of this work,
The Bibliotheca Britannica, but his versatility is evi-
denced by his medical works, his philosophical essays,
and his teaching of the medical arts.

Robert Watt was born on a small farm in the parish
of Stewarton, in Ayrshire, Scotland, on 1 May 1774.
He was the youngest of three sons born to John Watt,
a poor farmer in this hamlet some eighteen miles south-
west of Glasgow. The indomitable perseverance of
Robert Watt to obtain education and training admirably
prepared him for the formidability he was to show in
the compilation of *The Bibliotheca.* In 1793-95, he was
a matriculated student in the Arts classes at the University of Glasgow. He next transferred to the University of Edinburgh where he attended classes in Moral
Philosophy and Natural Philosophy. Chambers[1] tells
us that he was dissuaded from the study of Divinity
which he planned, and encouraged to turn to Medicine.
In the fall of 1796, after a summer's teaching in the
hamlet of Kilmaurs, he continued his attendance at
Edinburgh University taking courses in anatomy.

Necessity forced Watt to accept the position of paro-
chial schoolmaster in Symington, Ayrshire, and for
1797-98 his medical studies were interrupted. When he
returned to medical study he matriculated at Glasgow
University, and here in 1799 (April 6), he was made

---

1. Robert Chambers, *Lives of Illustrious and Distinguished Scotsmen*
. . . . 4v. Glasgow, 1835. Chambers remains the most important source
for the life of Watt, but see *Critical and Biographical Notices* generally.

a licentiate of the Faculty of Physicians and Surgeons. From 1799 to 1810 he remained in general practice at Paisley, and in these years he was made a member of the Faculty of Physicians and Surgeons, Glasgow (January 5, 1807); and on March 20, 1810 he was incorporated M.D. at King's College, Aberdeen.[2]

It was in Glasgow that Watt was to know great fame as a physician. He removed to this city in 1810. Here he was to know great honour, and for some seven years he was a dominant figure in the city's intellectual activity. On October 1, 1810 he had been made a member of the Glasgow Philosophical Society, and for the years 1816-17 he served as the society's president. From 1811 to 1816 he lectured on the Theory and Practice of Medicine in Glasgow University, and his reputation in the medical arts earned him the first presidency of the Glasgow Medical Society (1814-15). For two years, 1814-16, he served as president of the Faculty of Physicians and Surgeons of Glasgow. All of these capacities were assumed by Watt in conjunction with a very extensive private practice, and his attendance as physician to the Glasgow Royal Infirmary.

In 1817 poor health forced Watt to withdraw from practice. He retired to Campvale, a small town near Glasgow, where he supervised the completion of *The Bibliotheca Britannica*. He died here on March 12, 1819.

2. In some of the authorities (Allibone; *Catalogue of . . .. Surgeon-General's Office*, U.S. Army), Watt's degree is listed as from Edinburgh, 1803. This is incorrect. See J. Finlayson, *Robert Watt*, London, 1897, p. 11.

THE MEDICAL WORKS

Very soon after entering general practice in Paisley, Watt made some contributions to the London *Medical and Physical Journal*. In March 1800, his paper "A Description of a New Instrument for Operating for the Stone (with illustration)," was published, and in the same year, "A Description of a New Machine for curing Distorted limbs (with illustration)".[3] In the

same journal for May 1801, Watt wrote a letter on vaccine inoculation taking effect in those who have had small-pox, and on vaccinia and small-pox existing simultaneously in the same subject. In 1808, while still in Paisley, he published his *Cases of Diabetes, Consumption . . . with Observations on the History and Treatment of Disease in General*. This treatise was widely discussed and its observations accepted and rejected. Its wide impression is attested in the constant reference made to it in the widely used *Craigie's Practice of Physic* (Edinburgh, 1840). Watt, himself, answered some of the criticisms of it in the *Edinburgh Medical and Surgical Journal* of July, 1809. The treatise however is completely antiquated, and its interest remains only historical.[4]

In 1813 Watt published his *Treatise on the Chincough*, to which he appended "An Inquiry into the Relative Mortality of the Principal Diseases of Children." This appendix has known a wide impression and discussion. The research for this appendix consisted in the investigation of some fifteen manuscript folio volumes of registers for the various burial places of Glasgow. Watt found, as he had anticipated, that after the introduction of vaccination, the deaths from

3. See the bibliography for full titles. The second paper gave rise to a controversy in that journal with a Mr. Sheldrake of London.

4. See Finlayson, *op. cit.*, p. 14.

small-pox had been greatly reduced, and he expected to find proof of a corresponding reduction in infantile mortality as a whole. But his research showed that this was not so. He writes:

> To ascertain the real amount of this saving of infantile life, I turned up one of the later years, and by accident that of 1808, when, to my utter astonishment, I found that still a half, or more than a half, perished before the tenth year of their age! I could hardly believe the testimony of my senses, and therefore began to turn up other years, when I found that in all of them the proportion was less than in 1808; but still on taking an average of several years, it amounted to nearly the same thing as at any former period during the last thirty years. This was a discovery I by no means expected, and how it could have come to pass appeared to me inexplicable. (p. 335)

Further, commenting on his tabulation of the deaths for a series of years, Watt remarks:

> The first thing which strikes the mind on surveying the preceding table is the vast diminution in the proportion of deaths by small-pox: a reduction from 19.55 to 3.90; but the increase in the subsequent column (measles) is still more remarkable, an increase from .95 to 10.76. In the small-pox we have the deaths reduced to nearly a fifth of what they were twenty-five years ago; in the same period, the deaths by measles have increased more than eleven times. (p. 376) It must be admitted that while the small-pox were in full force, they had the power of modifying and rendering the measles mild, and now that they are in great measure expelled, the measles are gradually coming to occupy the same ground which they formerly did. (p. 378)

Watt's statistical inquiry and his induction founded on it were calculated to produce immediate hostile reaction. Even Edward Jenner referred to it with manifest annoyance.[5] Yet, Watt was a strong advocate of vaccination and he had foreseen that his figures might be used as an argument against cow-pox. In the preface to his treatise he made the issue clear:

> The Author has been told that the statements he has made are likely to produce injurious effects, in strengthening the prejudice of the vulgar. To this he would reply, that if prejudice is only to be suppressed by concealing the most important facts, he has no idea of purchasing its suppression at so high a price.

---

5. See a letter of Jenner quoted in Finlayson, *op. cit.*, p. 21.

Watt further replied to criticism of his tables and induction made in the columns of *The Edinburgh Medical and Surgical Journal.* In a letter to that journal, dated April 1814, Watt replies to his critics:

> Nothing could have induced me to embark in support of an opinion so contrary to established notions, but a conviction of its importance, and a desire to discover the truth. If you, or any of your readers, from the side I have taken, should think me hostile to cow-pox, I can assure you that you are mistaken. Indeed, that inestimable discovery has suffered much more from the forwardness of its friends, than the strength of its enemies. (*loc.cit.,* p. 177)

Dr. Farr, writing fifty years later, assessed the value of Watt's induction, and observed:

> It must be admitted that although there were defects in his data, Dr. Watt succeeded in showing (1) that small-pox was one of the greatest causes of death in Glasgow down to the year 1800; (2) that the deaths by small-pox were reduced to a fifth of their original number by vaccination; and (3) that the children died in nearly the same numbers as before, but of other forms of disease.[6]

The controversy of the acceptance or rejection of the tables and the validity of Watt's induction continued well along into the nineteenth century.[7]

Watt was a member of the Medical and Chirurgical Society of London, and a communication by him was read to this body on February 1, 1814. His paper dealt with a remarkable series of chronometric nervous attacks in a young girl, called by him, "Chorea." This paper is particularly interesting in the historical notices that Watt makes of superstition and nervous disorders.[8]

In the essays of the Glasgow Medical Society, there is a communication by Watt on Erysipelas which treats of the contagiousness of this disease. The cases he

---

6. *Letter to the Registrar-General on the Cause of Death in England.* London, 1867, p. 214. See also his *Vital Statistics,* London, 1885. Farr described Watt as "evidently a practitioner of great sagacity and a philosophical professor of medicine."

---

7. See the entries for Thomson, Creighton, McVail in the bibliography.

---

8. Watt points out that on June 10, 1697 three men and four women were burned at Paisley in connection with the Bargarran witchcraft case.

makes elucidation from had been drawn from his experience in the wards of the hospital.

Perhaps, Watt's reputation in the medical arts will ultimately depend on his fame as a teacher of the Principles and Practice of Medicine; and in this capacity his industry will be seen in his *Catalogue of Medical Books for the Use of Students attending Lectures on the Principles and Practice of Medicine.*

THE CATALOGUE OF MEDICAL BOOKS

In the winter of 1810, Watt had removed to Glasgow where he continued in practice. Here, in 1810 or 1811, he began to lecture on The Theory and Practice of Medicine. He had a large house on Queen Street, and he may have lectured there, or in the College Street rooms where Allan Burns, Granville Sharp Pattison, and Andrew Russell taught anatomy and surgery. Watt knew great success as a lecturer, and he hoped that his lectures would stimulate his students to further reading. In this hope he made available to his students his own medical library which he indexed and catalogued. The catalogue he published in 1812 under the title, *Catalogue of Medical Books for the Use of Students attending Lectures. . . .* To the catalogue he prefixed "An Address to Medical Students on the Best Method of Prosecuting their Studies," in which he observed:

> In my Lectures on the Practice Of Medicine, after considering the history and treatment of each disease, I give a list of the best authors who have written on that subject, and I now put it in your power to peruse these authors, to examine their facts and opinions, and to draw your own conclusions. (p. 6)

Watt had brought this library of medical works together very carefully, and in making it available to the student he had hoped to effect a synthesis of all the scientific literature to better enable the student a practical administration of his art:

> In fine, I have used my best endeavors to concentrate all the branches of Medical Science into one focus, and particularly to insist on those points, which I conceive to be of use to the Practical Physician.
> In forming the Medical Library, my conduct has been influenced by the same principles. In a Course of Lectures, it is only the outlines that are sketched, the blanks must be filled up by your own reading and reflection. On every branch of the Science, the Books will afford you an ample stock of original information; by diligence and application, make that information your own, and my intentions are accomplished. (p. 14)

In this utility of his library that Watt allowed his students, he followed the example of an older Glasgow Surgeon, John Paisley, who also had allowed his students the privelege of his unusually fine library.[9]

The plan, like Watt's, had been very successful.

Watt's *Catalogue of Medical Books* lists some 1000 publications. Most of these titles had been published in the eighteenth century, but quite a few are drawn from the seventeenth century, and some few from the sixteenth century. Watt was not preparing an inclusive list of medical books. As he observes in his *Preface,* the library was one of the "best" authors. Since, ultimately, the *Catalogue* was a guide to his library and the reading of the student, Watt attempted no critical annotation, but contented himself in the simple alphabetical enumeration of titles by authors. The *Catalogue* has immediate importances. The sagacious selectivity of Watt makes it the best enumerative bibliography of 18th century medicine available. For Watt's day this list remains the important medical literature available the practitioner and student. But the historical interests are even more important. The student of the history of medicine has, in this *Catalogue,* the best outline of the progress of the medical sciences that could be desired. It will be great credit

---

9. Paisley's student, the celebrated medical teacher William Cullen, later made Paisley's library available to his students.

to the medical library which, checking its holdings against Watt's *Catalogue,* can claim all its entries. We doubt that there is a library which can claim copies of all the entries.

The *Catalogue* has a further interest. There is no doubt that it was the genesis of the monumental *Bibliotheca Britannica.* In the index of the catalogue, unfortunately not printed, Watt had prepared a subject list for the volumes. Chambers tells us that the utility of this index soon led Watt to the consideration of a *Catalogue* that would embrace all medical works which had been printed in the British dominions. Soon he added works on Law, and the works on Divinity and miscellaneous subjects, and provision for foreign works was made as well. *The Bibliotheca Britannica* was the result.

PHILOSOPHICAL WORKS

In 1816 Watt was elected President of the Glasgow Philosophical Society. In this capacity, and indicative of his wide interests, he read to the Society on December 16, 1816, a paper on the "Natural History of Man." Chambers mentions a manuscript on *Light, Heat and Cold,* unfortunately lost, from which Watt had delivered extracts in communication to the Society. As early as 1814, Watt's philosophical interests had led him to the anonymous publication of a little book entitled, *Rules of Life, with Reflections on the Manners, and Disposition of Mankind.* This consists of some 1000 aphorisms. They had evidently been noted by Watt, from his desultory reading, in a commonplace book.

THE BIBLIOTHECA BRITANNICA

We have already noted that the *Catalogue of Medical Books* was the genesis of the *Bibliotheca Britannica.* In the beginning of 1817, Watt had withdrawn from practice. In a note on the back of the cover of Part I of the *Bibliotheca* (1819),[10] he tells us that "he saw himself verging towards the afternoon of life in an impaired state of health." The *Bibliotheca* was unfinished, and his withdrawal in 1817 to Campvale was ostensibly to allow time for the completion of his work.

In the note on the back of the cover of Part I, Watt further informs us that the project of the *Bibliotheca* had been kept in view for "nearly twenty-six years."[11] This would take us back before his medical classes of 1811, or his *Catalogue of Medical Books* of 1812. It would, in effect, take us back to his student days of 1793. There is no doubt that Watt had long contemplated his *Bibliotheca Britannica or General Index to British and Foreign Literature.* Originally, perhaps, he had intended only what is contained in the first two volumes, *viz.,* a dictionary of authors. The Index to Subjects for his medical library may have suggested the Subject portion of the *Bibliotheca,* contained in its last two volumes.

In Campvale, Watt continued the work on the *Bibliotheca* assisted by his sons; William Motherwell, the Glasgow poet; and by Alexander Whitelaw,[12] who edited the *Literary Casket.* Chambers tells us that he urged on the work, often directing the assistants from his sick-bed. An advertisement, dated December 1, 1818,[13] announced that the first portion of the work would be issued in February 1819. But when Watt died in March 1819, only a few sheets had been printed off.[14] The work had been prepared on the

10. The original part is in the Mitchell Library, Glasgow.

11. The preface to the completed work issued in 1824 talks of "unwearied care and indefatigable labour for nearly twenty years."

12. Whitelaw worked at many books issued by Blackie, the Glasgow publisher, amongst others Chambers's *Dictionary.* Since Whitelaw was associated with Watt, he must have supervised the biography of his friend in Chambers's *Dictionary.*

13. Preserved in the Mitchell Library, Glasgow.

14. Preface to the completed edition (1824).

basis of a list of subscribers. This list was issued with the second part of the *Bibliotheca,* and in some copies of the bound volume it is preserved. It contains over 400 names. Merchants, lawyers, members of the university in Glasgow are included, and some few physicians. The *Bibliotheca,* itself, under Watt's name, states that Parts I to IV, 1819-1820, were issued in Glasgow; Parts V to IX were issued in Edinburgh, 1821-1824.[15] The completed edition was issued in Edinburgh in 1824. The title on the boards of the original parts differs from the title of the completed work; it agrees with the title of Watt's ms. preserved in the Paisley Library. It runs as follows:

---

15. The Mitchell Library in Glasgow has the first two parts in the original boards.

THE

BIBLIOTHECA BRITANNICA

OR

A GENERAL INDEX

TO THE

LITERATURE OF GREAT BRITAIN
AND IRELAND

ANCIENT & MODERN

Including

Such Foreign Works As Have Been Translated Into
English Or Printed In The British Dominions

As Also A Copious Selection From The Writings Of
The Most Distinguished Authors Of All
Ages And Nations In Two Divisions

Vol. I Part I from AA to Ball incl.

By Robert Watt, M.D.

When Watt died, it was feared that his death might lead to the cancellation of the work by the refusal of the subscribers to continue their support. Accordingly, there was issued with the first part a circular assuring the subscribers that the work would be carried to completion.[16] There is no way of calculating the number of sets finally run off by the printers, Constable of Edinburgh, but our enquiries would suggest that, including the original issue in parts, there were some 400 complete sets made.

The manuscript of the *Bibliotheca* was found amongst the possessions of Watt's youngest daughter who died insane in the poorhouse in 1864.[17] The manuscript was on thousands of slips of paper bundled up, without order, in two large sacks. It was acquired by the Paisley Free Library, Scotland, where it now is, arranged carefully in a series of volumes, fifteen for the authors, and fifty-four for subjects. Watt had used the sheets of the author section for the compilation of the subject portion. This he had accomplished by copious deletions and the use of headings, and this accounts for the large number of subject volumes.[18]

The *Bibliotheca Britannica* is a universal bibliography. In no sense can it be classed a national bibliography. Volumes I and II contain an alphabetical list of authors and their works; volumes III and IV contain an alphabetical classification of subjects. In a sense Part II cannot be used without Part I, since the subject titles are not detailed but rather cross-referred to the author portion. It has been estimated that 40,000 titles are specified, but our study would fix the figure at upwards of 50,000. It is useless to talk of the many errors which are inevitable in such a work. The

16. The circular was signed by the divines, Ralph Wardlaw and Thomas Chalmers; by George Jardine, professor of Logic at Glasgow; and by James Ewing. It is reproduced in Finlayson, *op. cit.*, pp. 32-34.

17. See *London Reader*, 28 May 1864.

18. The ms. was purchased for the Paisley Free Library by a Dr. Richmond, empowered to do so by Thomas Coats.

individual who would make depreciation on this score is not bibliographer, and fails to recognize that Watt's work is only a point of departure; the verification of titles remains the chore of any bibliographer worthy of the name. Of course, Watt's plan is a little awkward, but with a little diligence it is practicable. The significance of Watt's work is realized only if we remember that but Brunet (*Manuel du Libraire*), and Grässe (*Trésor des Livres*) can be classed equal to it, and that the *Cambridge Bibliography of English Literature*, in a sense, continues it. The stature of the *Bibliotheca Britannica* is truly monumental.

As to the sources of Watt for the *Bibliotheca*, Watt himself has supplied the answer. These, and they run into hundreds, will be found detailed under the subject-heading "Bibliography," found in the second portion.

A BIBLIOGRAPHY OF ROBERT WATT, M.D.

PART I: PUBLISHED WORKS AND PAPERS

1. Books

2. Contributions to Periodical Literature

3. Manuscripts

PART II: BIOGRAPHICAL AND CRITICAL NOTICES

PART I: PUBLISHED WORKS AND PAPERS

1. Books

Cases of Diabetes, Consumption, &c. with Observations on the History and Treatment of Disease in General. Paisley: Printed for Archibald Constable & Co., Edinburgh, &c., 1808. 8vo. pp. 327.

Catalogue of Medical Books for the Use of Students Attending Lectures on the Principles and Practice of Medicine. With an Address to Medical Students on the Best Method of Prosecuting Their Studies. Glasgow: Printed by James Hedderwick & Co. To be had of J. Smith and Son, Brash and Reid, &c., 1812. 8vo. pp. 72.

Treatise on the History, Nature, and Treatment of Chincough: Including a Variety of Cases and Dissections. To Which is Subjoined an Inquiry into the Relative Mortality of the Principal Diseases of Children, and the Numbers Who Have Died Under Ten years of Age in Glasgow, During the Last Thirty Years.

> —quaeque ipse miserrima vidi
> Et quorum pars magna fui.—*Virg.*

Glasgow: Printed for John Smith & Son, &c., 1813, 8vo. pp. 392.

Rules of Life; with Reflections on the Manners and Dispositions of Mankind. Edinburgh: Printed by James Ballantyne & Co., For Longman, Hurst, Rees, Orme & Brown, 1814. Small 8vo. pp. 278.

Published anonymously, but advertised as by Watt, on the cover of the first part of the *Bibliotheca Britannica*.

Bibliotheca Britannica; or a General Index to British and Foreign Literature. In Two Parts. Authors and Subjects. Edinburgh: Printed for Archibald Constable & Co., Edinburgh; and Longman, Hurst, Rees, Orme, Brown, & Green; and Hurst, Robinson & Co., London. 4v., 1824. 4to. pp., First Part, 991. Second Part not numbered.

Originally had appeared in parts. Parts 1 to 4, Glasgow, 1819-20; Parts 5 to 9, Edinburgh, 1821-24.

2. Contributions to Periodical Literature

"Description of a new instrument for operating for the stone (with plate)," *The Medical and Physical Journal* (London), III (March, 1800), pp. 195-198.

"Description of a new machine for curing distorted limbs (with an engraving)," *The Medical and Physical Journal* (London), IV (August, 1800), pp. 93-97.

"Letters to the Editors," *The Medical and Physical Journal* (London), V (May, 1801), pp. 430-32.

On vaccine inoculation and Smallpox, showing that a previous attack of smallpox does not prevent vaccine inoculation from taking effect; and on the two diseases existing at the same time, and yet continuing perfectly distinct.

"Observations on the treatment of Diabetes," *The Edinburgh Medical And Surgical Journal,* V (July, 1809), pp. 287-298.

"On the treatment of Diarrhoea and Dysentery," *The Edinburgh Medical And Surgical Journal,* VII (April, 1811), pp. 241-243.

In letters dated from Glasgow, February 6 and 9, 1811.

"Cases of Periodical Jactitation or Chorea," *Medico-Chirurgical Transactions Published by the Medical and Chirurgical Society of London,* V (1814), pp. 1-23.

Read before the *Society* February 1, 1814.

"Observations on the influence of vaccination on other diseases and on population in general," *The Edinburgh Medical and Surgical Journal,* X (April, 1814), pp. 168-178.

"On the formation of the Rainbow," *Annals of Philosophy* (London), February 1819, pp. 131-33.

Letter sent to Editor, Professor Thomas Thomson.

3. Manuscripts

"Observations on the nature and treatment of Erysipelas," *Essays of Glasgow Medical Society,* Vol. 1, No. 1.

Read 17 January 1815. Ms. volume in the Library of the Faculty of Physicians and Surgeons, Glasgow.

"Observations on Cancer," *Essays of Glasgow Medical Society,* Vol. II, No. 1.

Read 16 January 1816. Ms. volume in the Library of the Faculty of Physicians and Surgeons, Glasgow.

Ms. of *Treatise on Chincough, with Tables of Mortality.*

This ms. volume was presented to the Glasgow Faculty of Physicians and Surgeons by Dr. A. D. Anderson, and is now in their library.

Ms. of *Bibliotheca Britannica.*

Carefully arranged and bound in sixty-nine volumes (fifteen of *Authors* and fifty-four of *Subjects*) and preserved in the Paisley (Scotland) Free Library.

An Abstract of Philosophical Conjectures; or an Attempt to Explain the Principal Phenomena of Light, Heat, and Cold, by a few simple and obvious Laws.

This ms. title is given by Chambers (see Part II), and repeated by Finlayson (see Part II), but until now it has not been found. It is supposed to have been written in 1805, when Watt was in Paisley.

PART II: BIOGRAPHICAL AND CRITICAL NOTICES

Samuel L. Allibone, *A critical dictionary of English literature and British and American authors.* 3v. and 2v. supp. Phila., 1858-71.
Bibliography with some notices of Watt's *Bibliotheca.*

P. J. Anderson, *Officers and graduates of the University and King's College, Aberdeen, MVD-MDCCCLX.* Printed for the New Spaulding Club. Aberdeen, 1893.
Notice of Watt's medical degree, granted 20 March 1810 in King's College.

Bibliotheca Osleriana. Oxford, 1929.
A brief notice of the *Catalogue for medical students*

Robert Chambers, *Lives of illustrious and distinguished Scotsmen from the earliest period to the present time, arranged in alphabetical order, and forming a complete Scottish Biographical Dictionary.* 4v. Glasgow, 1835.
The most valuable source for the life of Watt. The 1870 edition of this *Dictionary* omitted some materials from the memoir.

George Watson Cole, "Do you know your Lowndes?," *Papers of the Bibliographical Society of America,* XXXIII (1939), 1-22.
Some incidental considerations of Watt's *Bibliotheca.*

Charles Creighton, *History of Epidemics,* 2v. London, 1891-94. Vol. II, 652-660.
A discussion of Watt's mortality tables affixed to his *Treatise on the Chincough.*

Alexander Duncan, *Memorials of the Faculty of Physicians and Surgeons 1599-1850.* Glasgow, 1896.
Watt was President of the Faculty in 1814.

Faculty of Physicians and Surgeons, Glasgow.
Portraits of Watt are in the Faculty Hall. One is attributed to Reynolds.

James Finlayson, *An Account of the life and works of Dr. Robert Watt, author of the "Bibliotheca Britannica."* London, 1897.
A brief but authoritative life of Watt, with an important bibliography appended.

James Finlayson, "Medical bibliography and medical education: Dr. Robert Watt's library for his medical students in 1812," *Edinburgh Medical Journal,* new series, IV (1898), 344.

Glasgow Mitchell Library.
Deposited here are the first two parts of the *Bibliotheca Britannica* in the original boards. Prefatory note on paper back of covers which states plan of the work and reason for its issuance in parts.

Glasgow Herald, 22 March 1819.
A notice of Watt's death.

Index to the proceedings of the Philosophical Society of Glasgow. Vols. I-XX, 1841-89. Glasgow, 1892.
Notice of Watt's presidency.

William Keddie, "Early history and proceedings of the Society," *Proceedings of the Philosophical Society of Glasgow,* Vol. IV, pp. 101, 117. Glasgow, 1860.
Some notices of Watt.

William T. Lowndes, *Bibliographer's manual of English literature.* . . . New edition by Henry G. Bohn. 6v. in 11v. London, 1858-64.
In the preface Lowndes makes some notices of the character and the sources of the *Bibliotheca Britannica.*

London Reader, 28 May 1864.
A notice that Watt's surviving daughter died in the poor house.

John McVail, *Vaccination vindicated.* London, 1887.
A brief discussion of Watt's mortality tables affixed to his Treatise *on the Chincough.*

Duncan Macfarlane, "Parish of Stewarton," *The New statistical account of Scotland,* Vol. V (Edinburgh, 1845), pp. 730-31.
An early notice of Watt.

Peter Mackenzie, *Old reminiscences of Glasgow and the West of Scotland.* 3v. London, 1865-68.
Some notices of Watt in III, 633-40.

Thomas Mason, "A bibliographical martyr—Dr. Robert Watt, author of the *Bibliotheca Britannica," The Library,* I (1889), 56-63.

Memorial Catalogue of the Old Glasgow Exhibition, 1894. Glasgow, 1896.
Some notices of Watt.

John E. B. Mayor, "Watt's *Bibliotheca Britannica* and Allibone's *Dictionary," Notes & Queries,* 5th series, VI, 342-343.
See rejoinders, *ibid.,* 5th series, VIII, pp. 151-52; p. 178; pp. 238-39; p. 296.

Paisley Free Library
The ms. of the *Bibliotheca* is deposited here.

H. R. Tedder, "Robert Watt," *Dictionary of National Biography.*

W. White, *Story of a great delusion.* London, 1885.
Discussion of Watt's mortality tables affixed to his *Treatise on the Chincough.*

27

CATALOGUE

OF

MEDICAL BOOKS,

FOR THE

USE OF STUDENTS ATTENDING LECTURES ON THE
PRINCIPLES AND PRACTICE OF MEDICINE;

WITH

AN ADDRESS

TO MEDICAL STUDENTS, ON THE BEST METHOD OF
PROSECUTING THEIR STUDIES.

═══════

BY ROBERT WATT, M. D.

MEMBER OF THE FACULTY OF PHYSICIANS AND SURGEONS OF
GLASGOW, MEMBER OF THE LONDON MEDICAL AND CHIRURGICAL
SOCIETY, &C. AND LECTURER ON THE PRINCIPLES AND
PRACTICE OF MEDICINE IN GLASGOW.

═══════

GLASGOW:
Printed by James Hedderwick & Co.
TO BE HAD OF J. SMITH AND SON, BRASH AND REID, AND
WALTER DUNCAN, BOOKSELLERS, AND OF THE
PORTER AT THE CLASS-ROOM.

1812.

ADDRESS

TO MEDICAL STUDENTS,

&c.

————

IN prosecuting the study of Medicine, you are no doubt actuated by a laudable ambition to rise to eminence in that profession. Besides the personal considerations of an honest fame and a handsome income, you have the pride of upholding the dignity of a science, which, amid all the revolutions of society, has obtained the confidence and the esteem of mankind. Trusting that such are your motives, I shall attempt to direct your views to that path by which you may most successfully reach the objects of your pursuit.

Where a profession is followed, merely at the request of a relation, or to humour the whim or caprice of a parent, much excellence is not to be expected. Nor will your success be greater, though the profession be the object

of your own choice, if you are not animated
by the best of motives. You are not to hope
for success, because you see others arriving at
wealth and honours, and you would wish to
partake with them. If you desire to emulate
such characters, follow their example.

These men, whose respectability and wealth
you admire, obtained not the enviable situation
they now hold, because they wished to be rich
and respectable; but because they loved their
profession with ardour and pursued it with zeal.
The envy and spite of disappointed rivals may
tell you otherwise; but depend upon it, that the
industry which arises from a love of your profession, is the TRUE path, I may almost say the
ONLY path, which leads to respectability.

On the necessity and importance of a proper
medical education, it is unnecessary to make
many observations. Even the youngest among
you cannot be ignorant, that when he shall
engage in actual practice, the most important
concerns of mankind are to be entrusted to his
care. And he must also know, that in proportion to the attention which he has employed in
the study of his profession, the effects resulting
from his practice may be of the most opposite
nature. By neglecting the proper opportunities
of improvement, his fellow-creatures, his dearest
connections, his most valuable friends, may fall
the victims of his ignorance.—But if, by care

and skill, he can restore to health those afflicted with disease, he may reasonably expect to be rewarded and honoured by the living and grateful monuments of his abilities. It is not from having spent a certain number of years at schools of medicine; it is not from having repeatedly paid fees to the most eminent teachers, nor from the charm of degrees, diplomas, and other academical honours, that diseases are to be cured. No, it requires real medical skill, and that can only be acquired by diligent and unwearied exertion *.

The reading of the student is too often confined to systems and to compilations, which are generally the works of men of no experience, or of men writing under the influence of preconceived opinions. By the first, materials of little value are as readily selected as those of real importance; while, by the last, only such facts are recorded as go to support a particular theory. To obtain correct views in Medicine, it is necessary to have recourse to original authors, to such as write from actual observation, who have seen and treated the diseases they describe.

Many students, however, are neither possessed of such works nor have access to them. To remedy this defect, the present plan of

* Introduction to Duncan's Heads of Lectures.

establishing a Library is undertaken, and it is
hoped that it will meet the approbation of those
for whose benefit it is intended.

In my Lectures on the Practice of Medicine,
after considering the history and treatment of
each disease, I give a list of the best authors
who have written on that subject, and I now
put it in your power to peruse these authors, to
examine their facts and opinions, and to draw
your own conclusions.   The sooner you begin
to investigate such topics and decide for your-
selves, the sooner will you arrive at a true
knowledge of your profession.   You are thus
enabled to collect a stock of ideas, not the
tenets of this author or of that teacher, but the
result of your own research and discrimination.

An idea has too generally prevailed, that
there is little useful knowledge to be derived,
except from the writers of the present day.
It is the interest of every compiler to make
his reader believe so, to make him believe
that he has given him the sum and substance
of all that is worth being known on the subject;
but such assertions should be received with
caution.   One set of these authors may have
communicated all they knew of their predecessors; and another may have selected such
things as suited their own particular purposes;
but still much valuable matter is left behind.
Many important facts and observations are

entirely forgotten, and many more have been repeatedly trumped up as new, though well known and familiar to the ancients.

A blind zeal for antiquity long impeded the progress of science. A similar mischief is to be apprehended from a bias to the opposite extreme. Lord Bacon aptly observes, that " Medicine is a science which hath been more professed than laboured, and yet more laboured than advanced, the labour having been more in a circle than in progression." However we may excel the fathers of our art in the variety of our acquirements, we have never surpassed them in the great qualities of medical ability, patient observation of disease and skilful judgment respecting its course and termination. Hence, after having suffered ourselves to be more or less diverted from the true path of inquiry, by the dreams of enthusiasts and the reveries of system-mongers, we are glad to resume our march in the road which Hippocrates and Sydenham traversed with such signal caution and success. By comparing the practice of the ancients with modern improvements, we shall learn to appreciate justly the value of the latter. By marking the errors into which our predecessors have fallen, we shall be enabled to pursue, more steadily, the right method of research. By observing the operation of the events which have conduced to the advancement of

science, we may learn in what manner we can
most effectually promote its future progress. At
all events, we shall avoid the fault of ascribing
to ourselves the merit of discoveries and inven-
tions, which had been made in former ages;
but which, from the baneful influence of prevailing theories, had fallen into unmerited
neglect *.

In every age and in every Sect in Medicine
you will find many useful authors. Observe
their facts, however lightly you may esteem
their reasoning. In all cases, where it is
practicable, acquire information at first hand.
Scrutinize with accuracy, and form your own
judgment. It is this frame of mind, this faculty
of discrimination, which distinguishes the man
of genius from the dull imitator, the dogmatist,
and the empyric.

As to the history and even the treatment of
many diseases, the ancients may be recom-
mended as models for imitation. With regard to
the Principles of Medicine, they are extremely
defective. This may be partly attributed to their
imperfect knowledge of Anatomy and Physiology, and to their total ignorance of Chemistry;
but it was still more owing to their fruitless researches after occult and imaginary causes, in
place of such as were real and obvious.

* London Medical Review, vol. v. p. 29.

Reformation from these reveries has been slow and imperfect. Most of our Systematic Authors, and many of our Teachers, still cling to these imaginary Theories, as possessing an air of knowledge, and affording a more easy solution of difficulties, than the philosophical, but more laborious research into the changes of structure and the changes of function in the different organs.

As there is some peculiarity in the plan I follow in teaching the Principles of Medicine, I shall, for the information of such of you as have not attended these Lectures, subjoin the following outline of the Course:

I. The situation, the structure, and the functions of a particular organ, in a state of health, are described; in other words, its Anatomy and Physiology. For it has been too clearly proved, that every attempt to explain disease, without the aid of Anatomy and Physiology, has been vain and fruitless. The works of Galen, Paracelsus, Van Helmont, Stahl, Boerhaave, Brown, Darwin, and a host of systematic writers of less note, afford melancholy proofs of this truth; while the writings and dissections of Bonetus, Morgagni, Lieutaud, Portal, Hunter, Baillie, and Monro, remain splendid monuments of their indefatigable and invaluable labours. In place of long and mystical disquisitions on abstract and unmeaning Theories, our observations

are grounded on the change of structure and of
function in the various organs.

II. Pathology. This branch of Medical Science
has led to more confusion than any of the rest.
Where people speak contemptuously of the
Theory of Medicine, they generally refer to the
fanciful, and often foolish explanations, which
have been given of the nature of diseases. The
subject is no doubt mysterious, but not half so
much so as would appear from the Theories which
have been given. For this reason, I have aban-
doned the word Theory, and have substituted
Principles as a more appropriate term, the Course
consisting rather of a display of Facts, which
ought to form the basis of every Science, than of
Opinions which too generally lead to Error.

Pathology ought to be grounded on Anatomy
and Physiology. This part of the subject natu-
rally divides itself into three heads. To inquire
into the Causes, which are known to derange the
structure or the functions of a particular organ;
the Symptoms by which we discover the presence
and nature of that morbid structure, and morbid
action; and the Appearances which have been
discovered on Dissection.

In this manner, the whole system is discussed,
taking one part or one organ after another.
Hence, in this extensive circle, I have it in
my power, under one head or other, to describe
almost every disease to which the human body

is liable. By following such a plan, so far from leading you into a maze of hypotheses, as the Theory of Medicine has too often done, it is leading you to the true source of knowledge, the study of the human body itself.

To illustrate this part of the subject still farther, I have it in my power, through the kindness of my friend Mr. Allan Burns, to show you, from his Museum, specimens of many of the most remarkable organic affections.

" Were I to guess," says Dr. Hunter, " at the most probable future improvements in physic, I would say they would arise from a more general knowledge, and a more accurate examination of diseases after death. And, were I to place a man of proper talents in the most direct road for becoming truly great in his profession, I would choose a good practical Anatomist, and put him into a large hospital to attend the sick and dissect the dead *."

Dr. Hunter tried the experiment, and when I mention Dr. Baillie as the subject of it, you will be able to judge how far it has been successful.—Let me, therefore, exhort you to follow the ROAD Dr. Hunter has pointed out, and, though your success may not be equal to that of his pupil, you are sure to surpass those who take an opposite course.

* Introductory Lectures.

III. Chemistry is also a part of the plan. After describing the Anatomy, Physiology, and Pathology of an organ, I next give you its Chemical Analyses. By Chemistry, for instance, we know the component parts of hair, of bone, of muscle, of tendon, of cartilage, and of all the other solid parts of the body. By the same means we arrive at a knowledge of the nature of the blood, the bile, the saliva, the gastric juice, the urine, and other fluids; we can also analyse the products of certain diseases, such as calculi, tumours, incrustations, &c.

From this source of knowledge alone, we can determine, with no inconsiderable degree of certainty, the nature of disease, and the method of cure; for, although Animal Chemistry has not arrived at that degree of perfection which may be expected, yet it has solved many perplexing difficulties, and laid the foundation for many important improvements. The superiority of the practice of the moderns over that of the ancients, is, perhaps, more owing to our knowledge of Chemistry, than to any one circumstance. I, therefore, omit no opportunity, in so far as the present state of science will permit, of explaining to you the chemical reasons for prescribing the remedy, and the operations which may be expected from it. This leads me to the

IV. Division of the Plan. The Materia Medica. To be able to enter with advantage on a combat, you must know the number, the nature, and the strength of your weapons. One part of the study of Medicine consists in finding out the objects you ought to have in view; another, in selecting the means best calculated to fulfil these objects: hence, the classification of Medicines.

To render what is said on the Materia Medica as interesting and useful as possible, it is not given in an abstract system; but disposed under proper heads throughout the course. For instance, when treating of the stomach and a superabundance of acid in it, I then discuss the subject of Antacids. When treating of the kidnies and a deficiency of urine, I take up the subject of Diuretics; when on the skin, Diaphoretics, Rubefacients; on the intestines, Purgatives, Anthelmintics; and so of the rest. By this subdivision, and putting every thing into its proper place, I give you a practical view of the subject; and by doing it in a condensed form, I am not taking up your time in repeating what you ought to learn from the teachers of the Materia Medica.

V. In the last place, your attention is directed to the application of remedies, or to those leading Principles upon which the Practice of Medicine is founded. This is the grand object of all your studies. The other parts are useful, or otherwise, in proportion as they bring you nearer to this mark or divert you from it. In every stage, I point out to you how the knowledge of Anatomy, Physiology, Pathology, Chemistry, and Materia Medica, leads to the cure of diseases.—In fine, I have used my best endeavours to concentrate all the branches of Medical Science into one focus, and particularly to insist on those points, which I conceive to be of use to the Practical Physician.

In forming the Medical Library, my conduct has been influenced by the same Principles. In a Course of Lectures, it is only the outlines that are sketched, the blanks must be filled up by your own reading and reflection. On every branch of the Science, the Books will afford you an ample stock of original information; by diligence and application, make that information your own, and my intentions are accomplished.

QUEEN-STREET,
10th *February*, 1812.

LECTURES.

~~~~~~~~~

THE WINTER COURSES

Commence annually in the First Week of November, and
continue till the end of April.

The PRACTICE of MEDICINE at Nine in the Morning.

The PRINCIPLES of MEDICINE at Ten Forenoon.

~~~~~~~~~

THE SUMMER COURSES

Commence annually in the First Week of May, and
continue till August.

The PRACTICE at Seven in the Morning.

The PRINCIPLES at Ten Forenoon.

~~~~~~~~~

FEES.—A single Course, *Two Guineas;* to a former
Student, *One Guinea.*—Two Courses at once, *Three
Guineas;* to a former Student, *Two Guineas.*—A PER-
PETUAL TICKET to all the Courses, FIVE GUINEAS.

REGULATIONS
RESPECTING THE USE OF THE BOOKS.

I. Two Books or Volumes may be taken out at a time, and each must be returned within *two weeks;* if no application has been made in the interim, they may be again taken out for the same length of time.

II. Any Student who has written on a Book, shall forfeit his right to the Library; and if it be materially damaged, by writing or otherwise, he must pay the price of the Book or of the Set to which it belongs.

III. The Books are to be kept at the Students' Lodgings. Any one lending a Book, or leaving it at a Shop, or other Public Place, shall forfeit his right to the Library.

IV. The Books are given out and received at No. 60, Queen-Street, every *Saturday Evening, from 5 till 6 o'Clock.* This business can be transacted by the Student only.

V. To assist in making additions to the Collection, and in keeping the Books in repair, each Student is required to pay *Five Shillings* on having his name Enrolled for the Library, which, if he resides in the town or neighbourhood, entitles him to the use of the Books for *Six Months.*

CATALOGUE

OF MEDICAL BOOKS,

&c.

A

ABERCROMBIUS, DAVID. De Variatione ac Varietate Pulsus Observationes, 12mo.   Lond. 1685.

Aberdour, Alexander.   Observations on Small-Pox and Inoculation, 8vo.   Edin. 1791.

Abernethy, John.   Surgical Observations, 8vo. 2 vols.
          Lond. 1804.

Abernethy, John.   Surgical Observations on the Origin and Treatment of Local Diseases, 8vo.   Lond. 1809.

Abernethy, John.   Surgical Observations on Diseases resembling Syphilis, &c. 8vo.   Lond. 1810.

Abernethy, John.   Surgical Observations on Injuries of the Head and other Subjects, 8vo.   Lond. 1810.

Abernethy, John.   Surgical Observations on Tumours and Lumbar Abscess, 8vo.   Lond. 1811.

Accum, Frederic.   System of Theoretical and Practical Chemistry, 2 vols. 8vo.   Lond. 1810.

Adair, J. M.   On Fashionable Diseases, 8vo.   Lond. 1796.

Adair, J. M.   Philosophical and Medical Sketches of the Natural History of the Human Body and Mind, 8vo.
          Lond. 1787.

Adair, J. M, Medical Cautions, chiefly for the Consideration of Invalids, &c. 8vo.   Lond. 1787.

Adams, Joseph. On the Cancerous Breast, 8vo. Lond. 1801.

Adams, Joseph. Guide to Madeira, containing a short Account of Funchal, 8vo.   Lond. 1808.

Adams, Joseph. Syllabus of a Course of Lectures on the Institutes and Practice of Medicine, 8vo.   Lond. 1811.

Adams, Joseph. Observations on Morbid Poisons, Chronic and Acute, 4to.   Lond. 1807.

Adams, Joseph. Inquiry into the Laws of Epidemics, and Plans for exterminating the Small-Pox,   Lond. 1809.

Ægineta, Paulus. Opera Omnia Medica, a Guinterio, Cornario et Goupylo, 8vo.   Lugd. 1589.

Aiken, John. Biographical Memoirs of Medicine in Great Britain, 8vo.   Lond. 1780.

Aiken, Robert. Concise View of Facts concerning the Cow-Pox, 12mo.   Lond. 1801.

Aitken, John. Outlines of the Theory and Cure of Fevers, 12mo.   Lond. ——

Aitken, John. On Fractures and Luxations, 8vo. Lond. 1790.

Aitken, John. Elements of the Theory and Practice of Medicine and Surgery, 2 vols. 8vo.   Lond. 1782.

Aitkin, John. Navy Surgeon, or a Practical System of Surgery, Illustrated by Remarkable Cases, 12mo. Lond. 1737.

Alder, Thomas. Outlines of a Treatise on the Disordered States of the Lungs, 8vo.   Lond. 1804.

Alexander, William. Experimental Inquiry into the Causes which produce Putrid Diseases, 8vo.   Lond. 1771.

Alibert, J. L. Treatise on Malignant Intermittent Fevers, with Notes by Caldwell, 8vo.   Philadelph. 1807.

Allen, John. Summary View of the whole Practice of Physic, 2 vols. 8vo.   Lond. 1761.

Alley, George. Observations on the Hydrargyria, a Vesicular Disease from the Use of Mercury, 4to. Lond. 1810.

Alpinus, Prosper. De Praesagienda vita et Morte Ægrotantium, &c. a H. D. Gaubio, 4to.   Hamb. 1734.

Alston, Carolus. Tirocinium Botanicum Edinburgense, 12mo.   Edin. 1753.

Alston, Charles. Lectures on the Materia Medica, contain-
ing the Natural History of Drugs, their Virtues and Doses,
2 vols. 4to.   Lond. 1770.
Anatomical Examinations. A Complete Series of Anatomical
Questions and Answers, 2 vols. 12mo.   Lond. 1807.
Anatomy and Physiology, a New System of, with the Com-
parative Anatomy of Animals, 3 vols. 8vo.   Edin. 1795.
Andree, John. Essay on the Theory and Cure of the Vene-
real Gonorrhœa, 8vo.   Lond. 1777.
Andree, John. Cases of Epilepsy, Hysteric Fits, and St. Vitus'
Dance, 8vo.   Lond. 1746.
Andree, John. Treatise on the Venereal Distemper, with
Dissertations on Canine Madness, and on Consumptions,
8vo.   Lond. 1738.
Andriollus, Mich. Angel. Domesticorum Auxiliorum et Fa-
cile Parabilium Remediorum, &c. Tract. v. 4to. Venet. 1698.
Andry, M. Orthopœdia or Treatise on Deformities in Chil-
dren, 2 vols. 12mo.   Lond. 1743.
Angelus, Michaelis. Liber de Partibus ictu sectis citissimè
sanandis, &c. folio.   Tigur. 1555.
Arbuthnot, John. Essay concerning the Effects of Air on
Human Bodies, 8vo.   Lond. 1783.
Aretæus. Opera Omnia, a Boerhaave, folio. Lug. Bat. 1735.
Armstrong, John. Medical Essays, 4to.   Lond. 1773.
Armstrong, John. Synopsis of the History and Cure of Vene-
real Diseases, 8vo.   Lond. 1737.
Armstrong, George. Account of the Diseases most Incident
to Children, 8vo.   Lond. 1777.
Arnaud, George. Instructions for Persons Afflicted with
Ruptures, &c. 8vo.   Lond. 1754.
Arnaud. Memoires de Chirurgie, 2 tom. 4to.   Lond. 1768.
Arnold, Thomas. Observations on the Nature, Kinds,
Causes, and Prevention of Insanity, 2 vols. 8vo. Lond.1806.
Assalini, P. Observations on the Disease called the Plague,
the Dysentery, and Ophthalmia of Egypt, 12mo. Lond.1804.
Astruc, John. Treatise on the Diseases of Women, 8vo.
2 vols.   Lond. 1762.
Astruc, John. On the Diseases of Children, 8vo. Lond.1746.
Astruc, John. On the Fistula of the Anus, 8vo. Lond. 1738.

Astruc, John. Academical Lectures on Fevers, Lond, 1747.

Aurelianus, Cœlius. De Morbis Acutis et Chronicis, 4to.
Amstel. 1709.

Avicenna. Opera Omnia, folio, a Alpago.   Venet. 1544.

Ayscough. Account of the Nature and Use of Spectacles,
8vo. Edin. 1751.

B

Babington and Curry. Outlines of a Course of Lectures
on the Practice of Medicine, 8vo.   Lond. 1806.

Bacon, Friar. Treatise *De Retardandis Senectutis,* or a Cure
for Old Age. See Sinclair's Code.   Edin. 1807.

Bacon, Lord. History, Natural and Experimental, of Life
and Death; See Sinclair's Code.   Edin. 1807.

Badham, Charles. On the Inflammatory Affections of the
Mucous Membrane of the Bronchiæ, 12mo. Lond. 1808.

Baglivi, George. Practice of Physic and Dissertation on the
Tarantula, 8vo.   Lond. 1723.

Baillie, Matthew. Morbid Anatomy of the most Important
Parts of the Body, 8vo.   Lond. 1807.

Baker, Georgius. De Catarrho et de Dysenteria Londinensi
Libellus, 4to.   Lond. 1764.

Baker, George. Letter to, on Adhesions of the Lungs
to the Pleura, 8vo.   Lond. 1762.

Balfour. Treatise on the Influence of the Moon in Fevers,
8vo.   Edin. 1785.

Ball, John. Modern Practice of Physic, 2 vols. 8vo. Lond. 1768.

Bancroft, Ed. Nath. Essay on the Disease called Yellow
Fever, with Observations on Febrile Contagion, Typhus
Fevers, Dysentery and the Plague, 2 vols. 8vo. Lond. 1811.

Barbette, P. Opera Chirurgico-Anatomica, Lug. Bat. 1672.

Barchusen, Joh. Conrad. De Medicinæ Origine et Pro-
gressu Dissertationes, 4to.   Troj. 1723.

Bardsley, S. A. Medical Reports of Cases and Experiments
in Hospital Practice, 8vo.   Lond. 1807.

Barnes, Thomas. New Method of Propagating Fruit Trees
and Flowering Shrubs, plates, 8vo.   Lond. 1758.

Barry, Edward. Treatise on the Digestions and Discharges
of the Human Body, 8vo.   Lond. 1759.

Bartholinus, Th. De Insolitis Partus Humani viis Dissertatio Nova, 12mo. Hagæ. 1740.

Bartholinus, Th. Epistolarum Medicinalium a Doctis vel ad Doctos, Cent. iv. 4 tom. 12mo. Hagæ. 1740.

Battie, William. Treatise on Madness, 4to. Lond. 1758.

Baudelocque. System of Midwifery, translated by Heath, 3 vols. 8vo. Lond. 1790.

Bayne. Essay on the Nerves and the Doctrine of Animal Spirits, 8vo. Lond. 1738.

Beddoes, Thomas. Essay on the Early Signs and Prevention of Pulmonary Consumptions, 8vo. Lond. 1799.

Beddoes, Thomas. Researches concerning Fever as connected with Inflammation, 8vo. Lond. 1807.

Belguer, M. Dissertation on the Inutility of the Amputation of Limbs, 8vo. Lond. 1764.

Bell, Benjamin. System of Surgery, 7 vols. 8vo. Lond. 1796.

Bell, Benjamin. Treatise on Gonorrhœa Virulenta and Lues Venerea, 2 vols. 8vo. Edin. 1797.

Bell, George. Treatise on the Cow-Pox, 12mo. Edin. 1802.

Bell, John. Discourses on the Nature and Cure of Wounds, 8vo. Edin. 1795.

Bell, John and Charles. Anatomy of the Human Body, 4 vols. 8vo. Edin. 1797.

Bell, Charles. System of Operative Surgery, Founded on the Basis of Anatomy, 2 vols. 8vo. Lond. 1809

Bellinus, Laurent. Opuscula Aliquot ad Archibaldum Pitcarnium, 4to. Lug. Bat. 1696.

Bellinus, Laurent. De Urinis et Pulsibus, de Missione Sanguinis, de Febribus, &c. 4to. Lug. Bat. 1717.

Belloste. Hospital Surgeon, 2 vols. 12mo. Lond. 1732.

Bennet, Christoph. Tabidorum Theatrum sive Phthisios Atrophiæ, &c. 12mo. Lug. Bat. 1742.

Bennet, Christoph. On the Nature and Cure of Consumptions, 8vo. Lond. 1720.

Bennet, Thomas. Essay on the Gout, with a New Method of Cure, 8vo. Lond. 1734.

Benvenutus, Josephus. Commentariolum de Hydrophobia, et Aceto Vini, 8vo. Luc. 1757.

Berdmore, Thomas. Treatise on the Disorders and Deformities of the Teeth and Gums.   Lond. 1768.

Bergman, Torbern. Physical and Chemical Essays, 3 vol.
8vo.   Lond. 1788.

Berkeley, Rev. George. Siris, a Chain of Philosophical
Reflections, and Inquiries concerning the Virtues of Tar-
Water.   Lond. 1744.

Berthollet, C. L. Chemical Statics, with Notes, by Lambert,
2 vols. 8vo.   Lond. 1804.

Berthollet, C. L. Researches into the Laws of Chemical
Affinity, 8vo.   Lond. 1804.

Bicket, William. Practical Surgery, with Remarks on the
most Remarkable Cases, Cures, and Dissections at St.
Thomas's Hospital, 8vo.   Lond. 1740.

Birch, John. Essay on the Medical Application of Electricity, 8vo.   Lond. 1803.

Bischoff, Frederick. Treatise on the Extraction of the
Cataract, 8vo.   Lond. 1793.

Black, W. Historical Sketch of Medicine and Surgery,
from their Origin to the present Time, 8vo. Lond. 1782.

Black, William. Medical and Political Observations on
Small-Pox, 8vo.   Lond. 1781.

Black, William. Dissertation on Insanity, illustrated with
Tables, &c. 8vo.   Lond. 1800.

Blancardus, Stephanus. Opera Medica, Theoretica, Practica,
et Chirurgica, 4to.   Lug. Bat. 1701.

Blackburne, W. Facts and Observations concerning the
Prevention and Cure of Scarlet Fever, 8vo.   Lond. 1803.

Blackmore, Sir Richard. On Consumptions and other
Diseases of the Lungs, 8vo.   Lond. 1724.

Blackrie, Alexander. Disquisitions on Medicines which
Dissolve the Stone, &c. 8vo.   Lond. 1771.

Blair, P. Case of Mr. Baker truly stated, &c. 4to. Cork.

Blair, P. A Fair, Honest, and full Reply to his Case of Mr.
Baker, &c. 4to.   Cork.

Blake, Robert. Essay on the Structure and Formation of
the Teeth in Man and various Animals, 8vo. Dub. 1801.

Blane, Gilbert. Observations on the Diseases of Seamen,
8vo.   Lond. 1800.

Blizard, Sir William. Suggestions for the Improvement of Hospitals, 8vo. Lond. 1796.

Blizard, Sir William. Lecture on the Situation of the large Vessels of the Extremities. Lond. 1803.

Blumenbach, J. F. Essay on Generation, translated by Crichton, 8vo. Lond. 1792.

Blumenbach, J. F. Short System of Comparative Anatomy, by Lawrence, 8vo. Lond. 1807.

Boerhaave, Hermannus. Elementa Chemiæ, 3 tom. 12mo. Lips. 1732.

Boerhaave, Hermannus. Historia Plantarum, 2 tom. 12mo. Rom. 1727.

Boerhaave, Hermannus. Institutiones Medicæ, 12mo. Lug. Bat. 1717.

Boerhaave, Hermannus. Oratio de Commendando Studio Hippocratico, Habita, &c. 12mo. Lug. Bat. 1709.

Boerhaave, Hermannus. De usu Ratiocinii Mechanici in Medicina Oratio, 12mo. Lug. Bat. 1709.

Boerhaave, Hermannus. Praxis Medica, 5 tom. Petav. 1728.

Boerhaave, Herman. Experiments concerning Mercury, 8vo. Lond. 1739.

Boerhaave, Herman. Academical Lectures on the Theory of Physic, 6 vols. 8vo. Lond. 1766.

Boerhaave, Herman. Aphorisms concerning the Knowledge and Cure of Diseases, 8vo. Lond. 1724.

Boerhaave, Herman. Treatise on the Powers of Medicine, 8vo. Lond. 1740.

Bologninus, Angelus. De cura Ulcerum Exteriorum, Lib. 2. a Gesnero, Fol. Tigur. 1555.

Bonetus, Theoph. Sepulchretum, sive Anatomia Practica, a Mangeto, 3 tom. folio. Genev. 1700.

Bontius, James. On the Diseases, Natural History, and Medicines of the East Indies, 8vo. Lond. 1769.

Borthwick, George. Treatise upon the Extraction of the Chrystalline Lens, 8vo. Edin. 1775.

Bostock, John. Essay on Respiration, 8vo. Liverp. 1804.

Bostock, John. Remarks on the Reform of the Pharmaceutical Nomenclature, and particularly on that adopted by the Edinburgh College, 8vo. Liverp. 1807.

Bostock, John. Remarks on the Nomenclature of the New London Pharmacopœia, 8vo.   Lond. 1810.

Botanical Analogy, a Short Statement to recommend the Study of, 12mo.   Lond. 1784.

Boulton, Richard. Treatises on Gout, Kings-Evil, and Lues Venerea, 8vo.   Lond. 1715.

Boulton, Richard. System of Rational and Practical Surgery, 8vo.   Lond. 1713.

Bourne, Robert. Cases of Pulmonary Consumption, treated with the Uva Ursi, 8vo.   Oxford, 1805.

Bowen, G. C. Dissertatio Medica, de Sanguine Mittendo, 8vo.   Edin. 1810.

Boyd. Dissertatio Medica de Diabete, 8vo.   Edin. 1773.

Boyer. Lectures upon Diseases of the Bones, by Richerand, translated by Farrell, 2 vols. 8vo.   Lond. 1804.

Boyle, Sir Robert. Treatises on Specific and Simple Medicines, See Sinclair's Code.   Edin. 1807.

Bradley, Dr. R. Course of Lectures on the Materia Medica, Ancient and Modern, 8vo.   Lond. 1730.

Brande, A. E. Experiments and Observations on the Angustura Bark, 8vo.   Lond. 1791.

Brandish, Joseph. On the Use of Caustic Alkali, in Scrofula, and other Chronic Diseases, 8vo.   Lond. 1811.

Bree, Robert. Practical Inquiry into Disordered Respiration, the Species of Asthma, &c. 8vo.   Lond. 1807.

Brisbane, John. Select Cases in the Practice of Medicine, 8vo.   Lond. 1772.

Broomfield, W. Thoughts on Inoculation, 8vo. Lond. 1767.

Bromfield, William. Chirurgical Observations and Cases, 2 vols. 8vo.   Lond. 1773.

Brooke, R. Practice of Physic, 2 vols. 8vo.   Lond. 1771.

Brown, John. Elements of Medicine and Life, by Beddoes, 2 vols. 8vo.   Lond. 1795.

Brown, Andrew. On the New and most Effectual Method of Sydenham, in Curing Fevers, 12mo.   Lond. 1691.

Brown, Joseph. Practical Treatise on the Plague, 8vo.
                Lond. 1720.

Browne, Dr. Account of Cures, performed by the Cold Bath, 12mo.   Lond. 1707.

Browne, J. Essay towards forming a True Idea of the Fundamentals in Physic, 12mo. Lond. 1719.

Bryce, James. Account of the Yellow Fever, 8vo. Edin. 1796.

Buchan, William. Domestic Medicine, or the Family Physician, 8vo. Edin. 1802.

Burns, John. Popular Directions for the Treatment of Diseases of Women and Children, 8vo. Glas. 1811.

Burns, John. Observations on Abortion, 8vo. Lond. 1806.

Burns, J. Dissertations on Inflammation, 2 vols. 8vo. Glas. 1800.

Burns, John. Practical Observations on the Uterine Hæmorrhage, 8vo. Lond. 1807.

Burns, John. Principles of Midwifery, including the Diseases of Women and Children, 8vo. Lond. 1811.

Burns, Allan. Observations on some of the most Frequent and Important Diseases of the Heart, 8vo. Edin. 1809.

Burns, Allan. Observations on the Surgical Anatomy of the Head and Neck, 8vo. Edin. 1811.

Burnet, Th. Hippocrates Contractus, 12mo. Edin. 1685.

Burnet, Th. Thesaurus Medicinæ Practicæ, 4to. Lond. 1673.

Burserius, Jo. Baptist. Institutions of the Practice of Medicine, translated by Brown, 5 vols. 8vo. Edin. 1803.

Burton, William. Account of the Life and Writings of Boerhaave, 8vo. Lond. 1746.

Butter, William. Treatise on Angina Pectoris, 8vo. Lond. 1806.

Butter, William. Treatise on the Infantile Remittent Fever, 8vo. Lond. 1806.

Butter, William. Essay on the Various Effects of Blood-letting, 8vo. Lond. 1734.

Buttler, R. Essay concerning Blood-letting, and its Effects on the Human Body, 8vo. Lond. 1734.

Buxton, Isaac. Essay on the Use of a Regulated Temperature, in Winter-Cough and Consumption. Lond. 1810.

Buzaglo, A. Treatise on Gout, with Cases, 8vo. Lond. 1778.

Bywater, John. Essay on the History, Practice, and Theory of Electricity, 8vo. Lond. 1811.

* Baynton, James. Descriptive Account of a New Method of Curing Old Ulcers of the Legs, 8vo. Brist. 1799.

D

C

CABANIS, P. J. G. Revolutions of Medical Science and Views of Reform, 8vo. Lond. 1806.

Cadogan, William. Essay on the Nursing and Management of Children, 8vo. Lond. 1772.

Cadogan, William. Dissertation on the Gout and Chronic Diseases, 8vo. Lond. 1771.

Cæsalpinus, Andreas. Praxis Universæ Artis Medicæ, &c. 12mo. Tarv. 1606.

Canvane, Peter. Dissertation on the Oleum Palmæ Christi, or Castor Oil, 8vo. Lond. 1769.

Canvane, Peter. Dissertation on the Properties of Castor Oil, 2d Edit. 8vo. Lond. 1775.

Capoa, Leonardo De. On the Uncertainty of the Art of Physic, 12mo. Lond. 1684.

Carmichael, Richard. Essay on the Nature of Scrofula, &c. 8vo. Lond. 1810.

Carmichael, Richard. Essay on the Effects of Carbonate and other Preparations of Iron, in Cancer, 8vo. Dub. 1809.

Castellus, B. Lexicon Medicum Græco-Latinum, Roterd. 1557.

Catalogus Librorum ad rem Medicam Spectantium in Bibliotheca Academiæ Edinburginæ, cum Append. Edin. 1773.

Catherwood, John. New Method of Curing Apoplexy, 12mo. Lond. 1715.

Caton. Practical Treatise on the Prevention and Cure of the Venereal Disease, 8vo. Lond. 1809.

Caverhill, John. Treatise on the Cause and Cure of the Gout, 8vo. Lond. 1769.

Celsus, Corn. Aur. De Re Medica Libri Octo cum Comment. Brachelii, 4to. Lug. Bat. 1592.

Chandler, John. Treatise on the Disease called a Cold, 8vo. Lond. 1761.

Charmes, Pajot De. Art of Bleaching, 8vo. Lond. 1799.

Charter of the Royal College of Surgeons of Edinburgh, 8vo. Edin. 1778.

Cheselden, William. Treatise on the High Operation for the Stone, 8vo. Lond. 1723.

Cheselden, W. Anatomy of the Human Body. Lond. 1792.

Chevalier, Thomas. Treatise on Gun-Shot Wounds, 12mo.
Lond. 1806.

Cheyne, George. Essay on the Nature and Cure of Gout,
8vo. Lond. 1722.

Cheyne, George. Theory of Acute and Slow, Continued
Fevers, 8vo. Lond. 1722.

Cheyne, G. Treatise on the English Malady, 8vo. Lond.1735.

Cheyne, G. Essay on Sickness and Health, 8vo. Lond. 1725.

Cheyne, G. Method of Curing Diseases of the Body and
Mind, 8vo. Lond. 1742.

Cheyne, G. Essay on Health and Long Life, 8vo. Lond.1725.

Cheyne, John. Essay on the Bowel Complaints and Wean-
ing-brash in Children, 8vo. Edin. 1807.

Cheyne, John. Essay on Hydrocephalus Acutus or Dropsy
in the Brain, 8vo. Edin. 1808.

Cheyne, John. Essay on Cynanche Trachealis or Croup,
folio. Edin. 1803.

Cheyne, John. Pathology of the Membrane of the Larynx,
and Bronchiæ, 8vo. Edin. 1809.

Chirac. Three Dissertations on Wounds, 12mo. Lond. 1750.

Chisholm, C. Essay on the Malignant Pestilential Fever of
the West Indies, 2 vols. 8vo. Lond. 1801.

Christie, Thomas. Account of the Ravages committed in
Ceylon, by Small-Pox, 8vo. Chelten. 1811.

Churchhill, Thomas Furlong. Medical Remembrancer, or
Pharmaceutical Vade-Mecum, 12mo. Lond. 1810.

Churchhill, T. F. Guide to Health, or the Means of Preserving Health, and Preventing Diseases, 12mo. Lond.1810.

Cicero, Marcus Tulius. Cato, or an Essay on Old Age,
8vo. Lond. 1773.

Clare, Peter. New and Easy Method of Curing the Lues
Venerea, 12mo. Lond. 1780.

Clark, James. Treatise on the Yellow Fever, in Dominica,
in 1793—96, 8vo. Lond. 1796.

Clark, John. Papers respecting Fever-Wards, and the Cure
and Prevention of Infectious Diseases, 8vo. Lond. 1802.

Clark, John. Observations on the Diseases in Long Voyages
to Hot Climates, 8vo. Lond. 1773.

Clarke, M. A.   Directions for the Management of Children,
8vo.   Lond. 1773.
Clarke, Edward Goodwin.   Medicinæ Praxeos Compendium,
12mo.   Lond. 1807.
Clarke, E. G.   Modern Practice of Physic, 8vo. Lond. 1805.
Cleghorn, George.   Observations on the Diseases of Min-
orca, from 1744—49, 8vo.   Lond. 1762.
Clerc, M. Le.   Complete Surgeon, from the French, 12mo.
2 vols.   Lond. 1710.
Clifton, Francis.   State of Physic, Ancient and Modern,
8vo.   Lond. 1732.
Clutterbuck, Henry.   Inquiry into the Seat and Nature of
Fever, 8vo.   Lond. 1807.
Clyton.   Essay on Quackery, and the Fatal Effects of Quack
Medicines, 8vo.   Kings. 1805.
Cockburn.   On the Distempers Incident to Sea-Faring
People, 12mo.   Lond. 1697.
Cockburn, William.   On the Nature and Cures of Fluxes,
8vo.   Lond. 1724.
Colbatch, John.   Generous Physician, or Medicine made
Easy, 8vo.   Lond. 1730.
Colbatch, John.   Collection of Tracts, Chirurgical and
Medical, 8vo.   Lond. 1700.
Colbatch, John.   Extraordinary Cure for the Bite of a
Viper, 8vo.   Lond. 1699.
Colbatch, John.   Treatise on the Causes, Nature, and Cure
of the Gout, 8vo.   Lond. 1700.
Coleman, Edward.   Dissertation on Natural and Suspended
Respiration, 8vo.   Lond. 1802.
Collection of the Yearly Bills of Mortality, from 1657 till
1758 inclusive, 4to.   Lond. 1759.
Collin, Matth.   De Pustulis Miliaribus, 8vo. Vindob. 1764.
Communications Relative to the Datura Stramonium, or
Thorn-Apple, in the Cure of Asthma, 8vo.   Lond. 1811.
Conringius, Hermannus,   Dissertationes Academicæ Selec-
tiores, 12mo.   Lug. 1686.
Consumptive Habit, Letter on, from a Physician in the High-
lands to a Friend in London.   See Sinclair's Code. 1807.
Cooke, James.   Marrow of Chirurgery, 4to.   Lond. 1700.

Cooke, W. Practical Treatise on the Tinea Capitis Conta-
giosa, 8vo. Lond. 1810.

Cooper, Samuel. Critical Reflections on several Practical
Points Relative to Cataract, 8vo. Lond. 1805.

Cooper, Samuel. Dictionary of Practical Surgery, according to the Present State of Practice, 8vo. Lond. 1809.

Copeland, Thomas. Observations on the Principal Diseases
of the Rectum and Anus, 8vo. Lond. 1810.

Cornaro, Lewis. Treatise on a Sober Life, and Earnest
Exhortation. See Sinclair's Code. Edin. 1807.

Corp, Dr. Essay on the Operations of the Mind on the
Body, 8vo. Lond. 1791.

Corpulency, Cursory Remarks on, 8vo. Lond. 1810.

Cowper, William. Anatomical Tables of the Human Body,
revised by Albinus, fol. Lug. Bat. 1737.

Cox, Joseph Mason. Practical Observations on Insanity,
8vo. Lond. 1806.

Crawford, A. Experiments and Observations on Animal
Heat, 8vo. Lond. 1788.

Cribb, W. Considerations on the Use of Injections in the
Cure of Gonorrhœa, 8vo. Lond. 1773.

Crichton, Alex. Inquiry into the Nature and Origin of
Mental Derangement, 2 vols. 8vo. Lond. 1798.

Crine, George. On the Management of the Gout, and the
Virtues of the Plant Bardona, 8vo. Lond. 1758.

Crowther, Bryan. Rabies Piratica, its Symptoms, History,
and Cure, 8vo. Lond. 1810.

Crowther, Bryan. Practical Remarks on Insanity and Dissections of the Brains of Maniacs, 8vo. Lond. 1811.

Crowther, Bryan. Practical Observations on the Disease of
the Joints called White-Swelling, 8vo. Lond. 1808.

Cruikshanks, William. Anatomy of the Absorbent Vessels of
the Human Body, 4to. Lond. 1786.

Crumpe, Samuel. Inquiry into the Nature and Properties
of Opium, 8vo. Lond. 1793.

Cullen, William. Physiology, or the First Part of the Institutions of Medicine, 8vo. Edin. 1785.

Cullen, William. Nosology, or Diseases in their Classes,
Orders, &c. 12mo. Glas. 1811.

Cullen, William. Nosology, or Diseases Arranged in their
Classes, Orders, Genera, and Species, 12mo. Lond. 1808.

Cullen, William. Treatise on the Materia Medica, 2 vols.
4to.   Edin. 1789.

Cullen, William. Clinical Lectures, MSS. Notes from, in
1772, 4to.   Edin. 1772.

Cullen, William. First Lines of the Practice of Physic, 4
vols. 8vo.   Edin. 1796.

Cullen, Gulielmus. Synopsis Nosologiæ Methodicæ, 2 tom.
8vo.   Edin. 1795.

Currie, James. Medical Reports on the Effects of Water,
Cold and Warm, as a Remedy in Fevers and other Diseases,
2 vols. 8vo.   Lond. 1805.

Currie, W. Observations on the Causes and Cure of Remitting or Bilious Fevers, 8vo.   Philad. 1798.

Currie, W. Treatise on the Synochus Icterodes, or Yellow
Fever, 8vo.   Philad. 1794.

Currie, W. Memoirs of the Yellow Fever in Philadelphia,
in 1798, 8vo.   Philad. 1798.

Curry, James. Examination of the Prejudices usually en-
tertained against Mercury, 8vo.   Lond. 1809.

Curtis, Charles. Account of the Diseases of India, in the
English Fleet and Hospital at Madras, 8vo.   Edin. 1807.

Cuvier, G. Lectures on Comparative Anatomy, translated
from the French, by Ross and Macartney, 2 vols. 8vo.
                                        Lond. 1802.

D

Daly, Carolus. Tentamen Medicum De Teritibus et Lum-
bricis, 8vo.   Edin. 1790.

Daran, Jacq. Observations Chirurgicales sur les Maladies
De L' Urethre, 8vo.   Paris, 1748.

Darwin, Erasmus. Zoonomia, or the Laws of Organic Life,
4 vols. 8vo.   Lond. 1801.

Daubenton. Observations on Indigestion and the Efficacy
of Ipecacuanha, 8vo.   Lond. 1809.

Davis, J. B. Scientific and Popular View of the Fever of
Walcheren, 8vo.   Lond. 1810.

Davis, J. Ford.   Inquiry into the Symptoms and Treatment of Carditis, 12mo.   Lond. 1808.

Dawson, Thom.   Cases in the Acute Rheumatism and the Gout, with the Method of Treatment, 8vo.   Lond. 1781.

Dawson, Amb.   Observations on Hydatids in the Heads of Cattle, 8vo.   Lond. 1778.

Dawson, Amb.   Thoughts on the Nature and Treatment of Hydrocephalus Internus, 8vo.   Lond. 1778.

Dawson, G. P. Observations on the Walcheren Diseases which affected the British Soldiers in the Expedition to the Scheldt, 8vo.   Lond. 1809.

De Graff, R.   De virorum Organis Generationi inservantibus, 12mo.   Lug. Bat. 1668.

Degrees in Physic, a Letter on the Origin, Nature, and Dignity of, 8vo.   Lond. 1736.

Denman, Thomas.   Introduction to the Practice of Midwifery, 2 vols. 8vo.   Lond. 1794.

Denman, Thomas.   Aphorisms on the Application and Use of the Forceps and Vectis, 8vo.   Lond. 1807.

Denman, T.   Observations on the Cancer, 8vo. Lond. 1810.

Dewar, Henry.   Observations on Diarrhœa, and Dysentery, as they appeared in Egypt, in 1801, 8vo.   Lond. 1803.

Diabetes, A Mechanical Inquiry into the Nature and Seat of, 8vo.   Oxf. 1745.

Dickson, D.   Essay on the Possibility and Probability of a Child's being Born Alive, and Live at the End of the Fifth Lunar Month, 12mo.   Edin. 1712.

Dickson, Tho.   Treatise on Blood-letting, 4to.   Lond. 1765.

Dickson, Caleb.   Inquiry into the Nature and Cause of Fever, 8vo.   Edin. 1785.

Diemerbrœck, Isbrandus. De.   De Peste Libri, quatuor, 4to.   Aren. 1646.

Dimsdale, Thomas.   Present Method of Inoculating for the Small-Pox, &c. 8vo.   Lond. 1767.

Dionis.   Course of Chirurgical Operations, 8vo. Lond.1733.

Dioscorides, P.   Opera Omnia a Suraceno, fol. Lug. Bat. 1598.

Directions for the Poor in Fevers, with Plain Rules for the Management of the Sick, 8vo.   Pais. 1786.

Dispensatory, Compiled by Command of the Duke of York, for Military Hospitals, 8vo.   Lond. 1748.

Deccumanus, S. E. De Morbo Scurbuto, 12mo. Amst. 1720.

Dodswell. Observations on Hydatids in the Heads of Cattle and Sheep, 8vo.   Lond. 1778.

Domier, William. Observations on the Climate, Manners, and Amusements of Malta, 8vo.   Lond. 1810.

Dominicetti, B. Medical Anecdotes of the Last 30 Years, Addressed to the Medical Faculty, 8vo.   Lond. 1781.

Donaldson, Gulielmus. Dissertatio Medica De Rheumatismo, 8vo.   Edin. 1801.

Dondus, Jacobus. Enumeratio Remediorum Simplicium et Compositorum ad affectus ferè omnes qui a Chirurgo Curantur, fol.   Tig. 1655.

Douglas, Colinus. Tentamen Medicum, De Morbo Coxario, 8vo.   Glas. 1802.

Douglas, John. Animadversions on a Late Pompous Book, entitled Osteographia,&c. by W. Cheselden, 8vo. Lond. 1735.

Douglas, John. History of the Lateral Operation, for Stone in the Bladder, 4to.   Lond. 1730.

Douglas, John. Treatise on the Hydrocele, 8vo. Lond. 1755.

Douglas, Robert. Essay on the Generation of Heat in Animals, 8vo.   Lond. 1747.

Dover, T. Physician's Legacy to his Country, 12mo. Lond. 1733.

Drowning, a Physical Dissertation on, 8vo.   Lond. 1747.

Dufour, W. Practical Treatise on the Diseases of the Urethra, 8vo.   Lond. 1810.

Duncan, Andrew. Observations on the Operation and Use of Mercury, 12mo.   Edin. 1772.

Duncan, Andrew. Heads of Lectures on the Theory and Practice of Medicine, 8vo.   Edin. 1790.

Duncan, Andrew. Medical Commentaries, from 1773 till 1795 inclusive, 20 vols. 8vo.   Edin. V. Y.

Duncan, Andrew. Medical Annals, from 1796 till 1804 inclusive, 8 vols. 8vo.   Edin. V. Y.

Duncan, Andrew, Jun. Edinburgh Dispensatory, Edin. 1810.

E

EARLE, SIR JAMES. Observations on Hæmorrhoidal Excrescences, 8vo. Lond. 1807.

Earle, Sir James. Essay on the Means of Lessening the Effects of Fire on the Human Body, 8vo. Lond. 1803.

Earle, Sir James. Account of a New Mode of Operation for Cataract, 8vo. Lond. 1801.

Earle, Sir James. Practical Observations on the Operation for the Stone, 8vo. Lond. 1796.

Earle, Sir James. Treatise on the Radical Cure of Hydrocele by Injection, 8vo. Lond. 1805.

Economy of the Human Frame, upon the Principles of the New Philosophy, 8vo. Lond. 1739.

Edinburgh Practice of Physic, Surgery, and Midwifery, 5 vols. 8vo. Lond. 1803.

Edmondston, Arthur. Treatise on the Varieties and Consequences of Ophthalmia, 8vo. Lond. 1806.

Elliot, J. Elements of the Branches of Natural Philosophy Connected with Medicine, 8vo. Lond. 1786.

Ellis Daniel. Inquiry into the changes induced on Atmospheric air by Respiration, &c. 8vo. Edin. 1807.

Ellis, Daniel. Farther Inquiries into the Changes Induced on Atmospheric Air, &c. 8vo. Edin. 1811.

Enquiry, An Impartial, into the Legal Constitution of the College of Physicians in London, 8vo. Lond. 1753.

Essays and Observations, Medical, by a Society in Edinburgh, 6 vols. 8vo. Edin. V. Y.

Essays and Observations, Physical and Literary, by a Society in Edinburgh, 3 vols. 8vo. Edin. V. Y.

Essays, Physical, on the Parts of the Human Body and Animal Economy, 8vo. Lond. 1734.

Essays on the more Common West India Diseases, and their Remedies, 8vo. Lond. 1764.

Essays, Miscellaneous, on Rheumatism, Gout, and Stone, 8vo. Lond. 1722.

Etmullerus. Opera Omnia a Mangeto, 3 tom. folio, Gen. 1696.

Eustachius, Barth. De Partibus Semen Conficientibus in Viro Exercitatio Epistolica, 12mo. Lug. Bat. 1707.

Eustachius, B. Tractatus De Dentibus, 12mo. Lug. Bat. 1707.

Eustachius, Barth. Opuscula Anatomica, 12mo.Lug.Bat.1707.
Evans. Dissertatio Complectens Observationes Quasdam De
 Febre, 8vo.   Edin. 1790.

F

FABRICIUS, HIERON. AB AQUAPEND.   Opera Chirurgica
 Omnia, folio.   Lug. Bat.. 1723.
Facts and Observations, Medical, from 1791 till 1800 inclu-
 sive, 8 vols. 8vo.   Lond. V. Y.
Falconer, Magnus. Experimental Inquiries concerning the
 Red Particles of the Blood, 8vo.   Lond. 1777.
Falconer. Observations Respecting the Pulse. Lond. 1796.
Falconer. Observations on Cadogan's Dissertation on the
 Gout, 8vo.   Bath. 1772.
Farr. Essay on the Medical Virtues of Acids. Lond. 1769.
Farr, Samuel. Translation of Hippocrates Epidemics, with
 Notes, 4to.   Lond. 1780.
Farrell, Charles. Observations on Ophthalmia and its Con-
 sequences, 8vo.   Lond. 1811.
Fauchard, Pierre. Le Chirurgien Dentiste au Traitè des
 Dents, 2 tom. 8vo.   Paris, 1746.
Feijoo, B. G. Exposition of the Uncertainties in the Prac-
 tice of Physic, 8vo.   Lond. 1751.
Fernelius, Joannes. Universa Medicina, folio. Francf. 1592.
Ferriar, John. Medical Histories and Reflections, 3 vols.
 8vo.   Lond. 1810.
Ferrius, Alphonsus. Lib. iii. De Sclopitorum Sive Archi-
 busorum, Vulneribus, &c. folio.   Tigur. 1655.
Fevers, Reflections on the General Treatment and Cure of,
 8vo.   Lond. 1772.
Feyjoo, Father. Rules for Preserving Health, particularly
 with Regard to Studious Persons, 8vo.   Lond. ——.
Fienus, Th. Libri Chirurgici Duodecim, 4to. Lond. 1733.
Fizes. Dissertations on Suppuration and Ulcers, Lond. 1750.
Flemyng, Malcom. Discourse on the Nature and Cure of
 Corpulency, 8vo.   Lond. 1810.
Flemyng, Malc. Dissertation on Dr. James' Fever Powder,
 8vo.   Lond. 1760.

Floyer, Sir John. Physician's Pulse-Watch, or an Essay on the Old Art of Feeling the Pulse, 2 vols. 8vo. Lond. 1707.

Floyer, Sir John. Treatise on the Asthma, 8vo. Lond. 1726.

Floyer, Sir John. History of Cold Bathing, Ancient and Modern, 8vo.   Lond. 1732.

Ford, Edward. Observations on the Diseases of the Hip-joint, by Copeland, 8vo.   Lond. 1810.

Fordyce, Sir William. Inquiry concerning Putrid and Inflammatory Fevers, 8vo.   Lond. 1778.

Fothergill, John. Account of the Ulcerous Sore Throat, 8vo.   Lond. 1748.

Fothergill, John. Complete Collection of Medical and Philosophical Works, by Elliot, 8vo.   Lond. 1781.

Fothergill, Samuel. On the Painful Affection of the Nerves of the Face, commonly called Tic Douloureux, Lond.1804.

Fourcroy. Elements of Chemistry, and Natural History, with Notes, by Thomson, 3 vols. 8vo.   Edin. 1800.

Fowler, Thomas. On the Effects of Blood-letting, Sudorifics, and Blistering in Rheumatism, 8vo.   Lond. 1795.

Fraser, Henry. On the Use of the Viscus Quercinus, in Epilepsy, 8vo.   Lond. 1806.

Freake, A. Observations on the Humulus Lupulus, with its use in Gout, &c. 8vo.   Lond. ———.

Frewen, Thomas. Reasons against an Opinion that a Person Infected with Small-Pox, can be Cured by an Antidote, 8vo.   Lond. 1759.

Frewen, T. Practice and Theory of Inoculation, Lond. 1749.

Friend, John. History of Physic, from the Time of Galen, till the 16th Century, 2 vols. 8vo.   Lond. 1727.

Friend, John. Nine Commentaries on Fevers, and Two Epistles on Small-Pox, by Dale, 8vo.   Lond. 1730.

Friend, Johannes. Historia Medicinæ a Galeni tempore usque ad Initium sæculi Decimi Sexti, folio.   Lond. 1733.

Friend, Johannes. Emmenologia, folio.   Lond. 1733.

Friend, J. Prælectiones et Operationes Chymicæ, Lond. 1733.

Friend, J. Novem De Febribus Commentarii, 4to. Lond.1717.

Fring, P. Treatise on Phrensy, 8vo.   Lond. 1746.

Fuller, Francis. Treatise concerning the Power of Exercise in Preserving Health, and in the Cure of Disease, Lond.1728.

Fuller, Thomas. Rational Account of Eruptive Fevers, especially Measles and Small-Pox, 4to.   Lond. 1730.

G

GAHAGAN, GEORGIUS. Tentamen Medicum De Inflammatione, 8vo.   Edin. 1790.

Galenus, Claudius. De Fasciis Liber, a Vido Vidio Florentino Interprete, folio.   Tigur. 1655.

Galenus, Claudius. Methodus Medendi, folio. Paris, 1530.

Gall, Dr. New Theory of Physiognomy, founded on Anatomy and Physiology, by Hufeland, 8vo.   Lond. 1807.

Gardiner, John. Observations on the Animal Economy and on the Causes and Cure of Diseases, 8vo. Edin. 1784.

Gardiner, John. Inquiry into the Nature, Cause, and Cure of Gout, 8vo.   Edin. 1791.

Garengeot, R. J. C. Traite des Operations De Chirurgie, 2 tom. 8vo.   Paris, 1720.

Garlick, T. Essay on Gout, and Method of Treating Kings Evil, Dropsy, Leprosy Cancers, &c. 8vo.   Lond. 1729.

Garnet, Th. Popular Lectures on Zoonomia, or the Laws of Animal Life, in Health and Disease, 4to. Lond. 1804.

Gataker, Th. Essays on Medical Subjects, 8vo. Lond. 1744.

Gaubius, Hier. Dav. Libellus De Methodo concinandi Formulas Medicamentorum, 12mo.   Lug. 1739.

Gaubius, Hier. Dav. Institutions of Medicinal Pathology, by Erskine, 8vo.   Edin. 1778.

Geach, Fran. Observations on Baker's Essay on the Endemial Colic of Devonshire, 8vo.   Lond. 1767.

Geoghegan, Edward. Practical Observations on the Venereal Disease, 12mo.   Lond. 1801.

Geoghegan, Edward. On the Treatment of Ruptures, particularly in a State of Strangulation, 8vo.   Lond. 1810.

Gesnerus, Couradus. Observationes De Medicinæ Chirurgicæ præstantia et Antiquitate, folio.   Tigur. 1555.

Gibbons, Thomas. Medical Cases and Remarks on Jaundice and Hæmorrhagy, 8vo.   Sudbury, 1801.

Gibney, Joh. Disputatio Chemica De Æthere. Edin. 1790.

Gibson, John. Treatise on Bilious Diseases and Indigestion, 8vo.   Lond. 1802.

Gibson, Guliclmus. Dissertatio Medica De Gonorrhœa
Virulenta, 8vo. Edin. 1790.

Gibson, Benjamin. Practical Observations on the Formation
of an Artificial Pupil, &c. 8vo. Lond. 1811.

Gilchrist, Eben. On the Use of Sea Voyages in Medicine,
8vo. Lond. 1756.

Gillert, C. E. System of Mineralogy in general, with all
the Arts arising from this Science, 8vo. Lond. 1776.

Girdlestone, Thomas. Case and Historical Sketch of Diabetes, 8vo. Yarmouth, 1799.

Glass, Thom. Twelve Commentaries on Fevers. Lond. 1752.

Glissonius, Franciscus. Tractatus De Ventriculo et Intes-
tinis, &c. 4to. Lond. 1677.

Glisson, Francis. Treatise on the Essence, Causes, Signs,
and Remedies, for Rickets, 12mo. Lond. 1668.

Gooch, Benjamin. Practical Treatise on Wounds and other
Chirurgical Subjects, 3 vols. 8vo. Lond. 1767.

Good, J. M. History of Medicine in so far as it relates to
the Apothecary, 12mo. Lond. 1795.

Good, J. M. Dissertation on the Diseases of Prisons and
Poor-Houses, 12mo. Lond. 1795.

Goodwyn, Edmond. Experimental Inquiry into the Connection of Life with Respiration, 8vo. Lond. 1788.

Gordon, Alexander. Treatise on the Epidemic Puerperal
Fever of Aberdeen, 8vo. Lond. 1795.

Gorter, Johannes. De Perspiratione Insensibili Sanctoriana-
Batava Tractatus, 4to. Lug. Bat. 1725.

Gorter, Johannes. De Perspiratione Insensibili, Editio altera
aucta et emendata, 4to. Lug. Bat. 1736.

Gorter, Johannes. Medicinæ Compendium in Usum Exerci-
tationis Domesticæ Digestum, 2 tom. 4to. Lug. Bat. 1735.

Goulard, M. Treatise on the Effects, and Various Preparations of Lead, 12mo. Lond. 1772.

Gourlay, William. Observations on the Natural History,
Climate, and Diseases, of Madeira, 8vo. Lond. 1811.

Grant, William. Observations on the Nature and Cure of
Fevers, 2 vols. 8vo. Lond. 1779.

Grant, William. Observations on the Origin, Progress, and

Treatment, of the Atrabilious Temperament and Gout, 8vo.   Lond. 1779.

Greenfield, John.   Complete Treatise of the Stone and Gravel, 8vo.   Lond. 1710.

Greenfield, John.   Treatise on the Safe Internal Use of Cantharides, 8vo.   Lond. 1706.

Gregory, John.   Lectures on the Practice of Physic, MSS. Notes from, 2 vols. 4to.   ——— 1778.

Gregory, James.   Notes from his Lectures on the Practice of Physic, 3 vols. 8vo. MSS.   ——— 1797.

Gregory, Jacobus.   Conspectus Medicinæ Theoreticæ, 2 tom. 8vo.   Edin. 1788.

Grieve, James.   Translation of the Medical Works of Celsus, with Notes, 8vo.   Lond. 1756.

Griffith, Moses.   Practical Observations on Hectic and Slow Fevers, and Pulmonary Consumption, 8vo.   Lond. 1779.

Guido, Cauliacus.   Opera Chirurgica Omnia a Tagultio, folio.   Tigur. 1555.

H

HAEN, ANTONIUS, DE.   Ratio Medendi, 2 tom. Vind. 1757.

Hahn, Joannes Gothofridus.   Variolarum Antiquitates e Græcis Ærute, 4to.   Brig. 1733.

Hallaran, W. S.   Inquiry into the Causes of the Number of Insane, and the Cure of Insanity, 8vo.   Cork, 1810.

Hallè.   Treatise on Health, translated from the Encyclopedie Methodique. See Sinclair's Code.   Edin. 1807.

Hallar, M. A.   Dissertation on the Sensible and Irritable Parts of Animals, 8vo.   Lond. 1755.

Haller, Albertus Von.   First Lines of Physiology. Edin.1801.

Halliday, Andrew.   Observations on the Causes, Nature, and Cure of Emphysema, 8vo.   Lond. 1807.

Hamilton, Sir D.   Treatise on the Miliary Fever, with a Collection of Cases, 8vo.   Lond. 1787.

Hamilton, Alexander.   Outlines of the Theory and Practice of Midwifery, 8vo.   Lond. 1796.

Hamilton, Alexander.   Letters to Osborn on the Practice of Midwifery, 8vo.   Edin. 1792.

Hamilton, James. On the Utility and Administration of Purgative Medicines, 8vo. Edin. 1808.

The same Book, 4th edition. Edin. 1812.

Hamilton, Robert. Duties of a Regimental Surgeon considered, with Observations on his general Qualifications, 2 vols. 8vo. Lond. 1794.

Hamilton, Robert. Letters on the Cause and Treatment of the Gout, 8vo. Lynn. 1806.

Hamilton, William. On the Preparation, Utility, and Administration of Digitalis, 8vo. Lond. 1807.

Hamilton, James. Hints for the Treatment of the Principal Diseases of Infancy and Childhood, 8vo. Edin. 1809.

Harper. Treatise on the Nature, Causes, and Cure, of Insanity, 8vo. Lond. 1789.

Harrington, Robert. Enquiry into the First and General Principles of Animal and Vegetable Life, &c. Lond. 1781.

Harris, Gaulterus. De Morbis Acutis Infantum. Lond. 1689.

Harris, Thomas. Treatise on the Effects of Crude Mercury, 8vo. Lond. 1734.

Harrison, Edward. Sketch of a Bill for the Improvement of Medicine, Surgery, &c. 8vo. Glas. 1810.

Hartley, David. Observations on Man, his Frame, his Duty, and his Expectations, 3 vols. 8vo. Lond. 1801.

Harty, William. Observations on Simple Dysentery and its Combinations, 8vo. Lond. 1805.

Haslam, John. Observations on Madness and Melancholy, with Cases and Dissections, 8vo. Lond. 1809.

Haslam, John. Illustrations of Madness, Exhibiting a Singular Case of Insanity, 8vo. Lond. 1810.

Hayes, Thomas. Address on the Danger of Neglecting Coughs and Colds, 8vo. Lond. 1786.

Haygarth, John. Letter to Dr. Percival on the Prevention of Infectious Fevers, 8vo. Bath, 1801.

Haygarth, John. Clinical History of Acute Rheumatism, and Nodosity of the Joints, 8vo. Bath, 1805.

Heberden, William. Commentaries on the History and Cure of Diseases, 8vo. Lond. 1806.

Heberden, William. Epitome of the Diseases Incident to Children, 12mo. Lond. 1807.

Heister, Laurence.   Medical, Chirurgical, and Anatomical
Cases and Observations, 4to.   Lond. 1755.

Heister, Laurence.   Compendium of the Practice of Physic,
8vo.   Lond. 1757.

Heister, Laurence.   General System of Surgery, 2 vols.
4to.   Lond. 1748.

Helmont, J. B. Van.   Ternary of Paradoxes, by Charleton,
4to.   Lond. 1650.

Helmont, J. B. Van.   Physic Refined, the Errors therein
Refuted, and the Whole Art Reformed, folio, Lond. 1662.

Henderson, Stewart.   Suggestions for the Prevention of the
Yellow Fever, &c. 8vo.   Lond. 1808.

Hendy, James.   Treatise on the Glandular Disease of Bar-
badoes, 8vo.   Lond. 1784.

Henry, William.   Elements of Experimental Chemistry, 2
vols. 8vo.   Lond. 1810.

Henry, William.   Analysis of British and Foreign Salts,
4to.   Lond. 1810.

Heurnius, J.   In Aphorismos Hippocratis, Lug. Bat. 1536.

Hewson, William.   Experimental Inquiries into the Nature
of the Blood, 8vo.   Lond. 1780.

Hey, William.   Practical Observations in Surgery, Illustrated by Cases, 8vo.   Lond. 1810.

Hey, William.   Observations on the Nature and Properties
of the blood, 8vo.   Lond. 1779.

Hildanus, Gul. Fab. Description of the Stone in the Bladder,
and the Several Ways of Operating, 12mo.   Lond. 1640.

Hildanus, Gul. Fab.   Opera Observationum et Curationum
Medico-Chirurgicarum quæ Extant Omnia,   Franc. 1646.

Hill, John.   Account of the Mushroom Stone and Violet
Stone, Plates, 8vo.   Lond. 1758.

Hill, John.   On Valerian, or the Virtues of that Plant in
Nervous Disorders, 8vo.   Lond. 1758.

Hippocrates.   Opera Omnia quæ Extant, Gr. et Lat.
a Fœsio, folio.   Francf. 1624.

Hippocrates.   De Morbis Popularibus, Lib. i. et iii. his
Accommodavit Novem De Febribus Commentarios Johan.
Friend, folio.   Lond. 1733.

History of Ruptures and Rupture-Cures, thoroughly considered, 8vo. Lond. 1726.

Hodges, Phineas. Strictures on the Elementa Medicinæ of Brown, 12mo. Lond. 1795.

Hodges, Nathaniel. Historical Account of the Plague in London, 8vo. Lond. 1720.

Hoffman, Fred. System of the Practice of Medicine, by Duncan, 2 vols. 8vo. Lond. 1783.

Hollerius, Jacobus. Liber De Materia Chirurgica a Gesnero, fol. Tigur. 1550.

Holwell, J. Z. Account of the Manner of Inoculating Small-Pox in the East Indies, 8vo. Lond. 1767.

Home, Franciscus. Methodus Materiæ Medicæ. Edin. 1793.

Home, Franciscus. Principia Medicinæ, 8vo. Edin. 1762.

Home, Francis. Inquiry into the Nature, Causes and Cure of the Croup, 8vo. Edin. 1765.

Home, Francis. Clinical Experiments, Histories, and Dissections, 8vo. Lond. 1783.

Home, Everard. Observations on the Treatment of Strictures in the Urethra, and Œsophagus, 2 vols. 8vo. Lond. 1803.

Home, Everard. Practical Observations on the Treatment of Ulcers on the Legs, 8vo. Lond. 1801.

Home, Everard. Observations on Cancer, connected with Histories of the Disease, 8vo. Lond. 1805.

Home, Everard. Practical Observations on the Treatment of the Diseases of the Prostate Gland, 8vo. Lond. 1811.

Hooper, Robert. Examinations in Anatomy, Physiology, Practice of Physic, Materia Medica, &c. Lond. 1812.

Hooper, Robert. On the Epidemical Diseases now Prevailing in London, 8vo. Lond. 1803.

Hooper, R. Compendious Medical Dictionary, Lond. 1801.

Horne, Joannes Van. Brevis Manuductio ad Historiam Corporis Humani, 12mo. Lug. 1665.

Horsburgh, William. Experiments and Observations on the Hartfell-Spaw, 8vo. Edin. 1754.

Howard, John. Practical Observations on the Natural History, and Cure of the Venereal Disease, 2 vols. Lond. 1806.

Howard, John. Practical Observations on Cancer, 8vo. Lond. 1811.

F

Hull, John. Essay on Phlegmasia Delens, Peritonitis Puer-
peralis and Conjunctivea, 8vo.   Lond. 1801.

Hulme, Nathaniel. Proposal for Preventing the Scurvy, in
the British Navy, 8vo.   Lond. 1768.

Hulme, Nathaniel. Libellus De Natura, Causa, Curationeque
Scorbuti, 8vo.   Lond. 1768.

Hulme, Nathaniel. Treatise on the Puerperal Fever, illustrated by Dissections, 8vo.   Lond. 1772.

Hume, Gustavus. Observations on the Angina Pectoris,
Gout, and Cow-Pox, 8vo.   Dub. 1804.

Hume, John. On the Bilious or Yellow Fever, and the
Remitting and Intermitting Fevers of the West Indies,
8vo.   Lond. 1778.

Hunter, William. Two Introductory Lectures, delivered to
his Last Anatomical Course, 4to.   Lond. 1784.

Hunter, John. Treatise on the Blood, Inflammation, and
Gun-Shot Wounds, 4to.   Lond. 1794.

Hunter, John. Treatise on the Venereal Disease, with
Notes, by Adams, 8vo.   Lond. 1810.

Hunter, John. Observations on the Diseases of the Army.
in Jamaica, and on the Means of Preserving Health in that
Climate, 8vo.   Lond. 1796.

Hunter, John. On the Diseases of the Army, in Jamaica,
and the Hepatitis of the East Indies, 8vo.   Lond. 1808.

Hurlock, Joseph. Practical Treatise on Dentition, or the
Breeding of Teeth in Children, 8vo.   Lond. 1742.

Hutchinson, Benjamin. Biographia Medica, or Lives of
Eminent Medical Men, 2 vols. 8vo.   Lond. 1799.

Hutchison, Alex. Copland. On the Operation for Popliteal
Aneurism, 8vo.   Lond. 1811.

Huxham, Johannes. De Aëre et Morbis Epidemicis, 2 tom.
8vo.   Lond. 1752.

Huxham, John. Medical and Chemical Observations on
Antimony, 8vo.   Lond. 1756.

Huxham, John. Dissertation on the Malignant Ulcerous
Sore-Throat, 8vo.   Lond. 1750.

Huxham, John. Essays on Fevers, Small-Pox, Pleurisies,
&c. 8vo.   Lond. 1750.

I

Jackson, Robert. Treatise on the Fevers of Jamaica, and America, 8vo. Lond. 1791.

Jackson, Robert. Exposition of the Practice of Cold Affusion, as a Remedy in Fever, 8vo. Edin. 1808.

James, R. On the Presages of Life and Death in Diseases, 2 vols. 8vo. Lond. 1746.

James, R. Modern Practice of Physic, as improved by Boerhaave and Hoffman, 2 vols. 8vo. Lond. 1746.

Jamieson, Thomas. Essays on the Changes of the Human Body, at its Different Ages, 8vo. Lond. 1811.

Imison, John. Familiar Introduction to Natural Philosophy and Chemistry, 2 vols. Lond. 1803.

Infirmary, the History and Statutes of the Edinburgh Royal, 8vo. Edin. 1749.

Infirmary, History, Statutes, and Rules, of the Newcastle upon Tyne, 12mo. Newcas. 1801.

Information for the Hair-Dressers of Edinburgh, against the Barber-chirurgions, 8vo. Edin. 1758.

Ingram. On the Gout, with Extraordinary Cases in the Head, Stomach, and Extremities, 12mo. Lond. 1767.

Inoculation, Reasons for introducing into Bury. Lond. 1733.

Johnson, C. T. Practical Essay on the Nature and Treatment of Cancer, 8vo. Lond. 1810.

Johnston, Henry. Practical Observations on Urinary Gravel and Stone; Diseases of the Bladder, Prostate Gland and Urethra, 8vo. Edin. 1806.

Johnstone, James. Essay on the Use of the Ganglions of the Nerves, 8vo. Shrews. 1771.

Johnstone, J. Treatise on the Malignant Angina, or Putrid Sore Throat, &c. 8vo. Worcest. 1779.

Jones, E. G. Account of the Remarkable Effects of Eau Medicinale in Gout, 12mo. Lond. 1810.

Jones, Gale. Observations on the Nature and Treatment of Hooping-cough, 8vo. Lond. 1794.

Jones, Robert. Inquiry into the State of Medicine on the Principles of Inductive Philosophy, 8vo. Edin. 1781.

Jones, J. F. D. On the Process of Nature in Suppressing Hæmorrhage from Divided and Punctured Arteries, 8vo. Lond. 1809.

Journal. The Medical and Physical, from 1799, till 1811, inclusive, 26 vols. 8vo.   Lond. V. Y.

Journal, The Edinburgh Medical and Surgical, from 1805, till 1811, inclusive, 7 vols. 8vo.   Edin. V. Y.

Irvine, Ralph. Experiments on the Red and Quilled Peruvian Bark, 8vo.   Edin. 1785.

Irvine, William. Observations upon Diseases, chiefly as they occur in Sicily, 8vo.   Lond. 1810.

K

KANT. Treatise on the Art of Preventing Diseases, 8vo. See Sinclair's Code.   Edin. 1807.

Keate, T. Cases of Hydrocele, Hernia Vesicæ Urinariæ and Hernia Incarcerata, 8vo.   Lond. 1788.

Keate, T. Cases of the Hydrocele with Observations on a Peculiar Method of Treating this Disease, 8vo. Lond.1788.

Keill, James. Essays on Several Parts of the Animal Economy, 8vo.   Lond. 1717.

Keill, James. On Animal Secretion and Muscular Motion, 12mo.   Lond. 1708.

Kentish, Edward. Essay on Warm and Vapour Baths, and on Scrofula and Pulmonic Complaints, 8vo.   Lond. 1809.

Kierman, F. Treatise and Observations on the Nature and Treatment of the Venereal Disease, 12mo.   Lond. 1811.

King, John. Essay on the Usefulness and Operation of Hot and Cold Bathing, 8vo.   Lond. 1737.

Kinglake, Robert. On Gout, exhibiting a View of its Origin, Nature, Cause, Cure, and Prevention, 8vo. Lond. 1804.

Kirby. Tables of the Materia Medica, 12mo.   Edin. 1805.

Kirkland, Thomas. Essay on the Cure of Diseases, which are the Cause of Fevers, 8vo.   Lond. 1767.

Kirkland, Thomas. Commentary on Apoplectic and Paralytic Affections, &c. 8vo.   Lond. 1792.

Kirkpatrick, J. History, Theory, and Practice of Inoculation, 8vo.   Lond. 1761.

Kirwan, R. Elements of Mineralogy, 2 vols. 8vo. Lond.1794.

Klaproth, M. H. Analytical Essays for Promoting the Knowledge of Mineral Substances, 8vo.   Lond. 1801.

Knight, Thomas. Vindication of a Late Essay, on the translation of the Blood, 8vo. Lond. 1731.

Kyperus, Albertus. Institutiones Medicæ. Amst. 1654.

L

LAMBE, WILLIAM. Medical and Experimental Inquiry into Constitutional Diseases, 8vo. Lond. 1805.

Lancet, Lemuel. Medico-Metrical Addresses to Students at Edinburgh, 8vo. Lond. 1801.

Lancisius, Jo. Mar. De Subitaneis Mortibus Libri Duo, 12mo. Rom. 1709.

Langius, Johannes. Themeta Chirurgica undecim a Gesnero, folio. Tigur. 1551.

Langrish, Browne. Physical Experiments upon Brutes, to Discover a Method of Dissolving the Stone. Lond. 1746.

Latham, John. Letter on Rheumatism and Gout, addressed to Sir George Baker, 8vo. Lond. 1796.

Latham, John. Facts and Opinions concerning Diabetes, 8vo. Lond. 1811.

Lavoisier, A. L. Elements of Chemistry, Translation of, with Notes, by Kerr, 8vo. Edin. 1796.

Lawrence, William. Anatomical and Practical Treatise on Ruptures, 8vo. Lond. 1810.

Leake, John. On the Lisbon Diet Drink, 8vo. Lond. 1797.

Leake, John. Medical Instructions concerning the Chronic Diseases of Women, 8vo. Lond. 1777.

Le Clerc, Daniel. History of Physick, 8vo. Lond. 1699.

Le Dran, Henry Francis. Parallel of the Different Methods of Extracting the Stone, by Dale, 8vo. Lond. 1731.

Le Dran, Henry Francis. Operations in Surgery, with plates, 8vo. Lond. 1768.

Le Dran, Henry Francis. Observations in Surgery, containing One hundred and fifteen Cases, 8vo. Lond. 1758.

Lee, James. Introduction to Botany, 8vo. Edin. 1796.

Le Fevre, Johannes Franciscus. Opera Medica Omnia, 2 tom. 4to. Vesun. 1737.

L'Emery, Nic. Cours De Chymie, Countinant la Maniere de faire les Operations qui sont en Usage dan la Medicine, par une Methode facile, 8vo. Paris, 1647.

Lemery, Nicolas. Traité Universel des Droguis Simples, 4to. Amst. 1716.

Lempriere, William. Practical Observations on the Diseases of the Army in Jamaica, 2 vols. 8vo. Lond. 1799.

Leslie, Dugud. Philosophical Inquiry into the Cause of Animal Heat, 8vo. Lond. 1788.

Leslie, John. Experimental Inquiry into the Nature and Propagation of Heat, 8vo. Lond. 1804.

Letters on the Force of Imagination in Pregnant Women, showing it to be a ridiculous Prejudice, 12mo. Lond. 1765.

Levison, G. Essay on the Blood, 8vo. Lond. 1776.

Lewis, William. Experimental History of the Materia Medica, 4to. Lond. 1761.

Libri duo De Recondita Febrium Intermittentium tum Remittentium Natura et Curatione, 8vo. Amst. 1759.

Lieutaud, Joseph. Precis De la Medicine Practique, 8vo. Paris, 1761.

Lieutaud, Joseph. Historia Anatomico-Medica, 2 tom. 4to. Paris, 1767.

Liger, C. L. Treatise on the Gout, 8vo. Lond. 1760.

Lind, James. Essay on the Diseases Incidental to Europeans in Hot Climates, 8vo. Lond. 1808.

Lind, James. Essay on Preserving the Health of Seamen, &c. 8vo. Lond. 1778.

Lind, James. Treatise on the Scurvy, 8vo. Lond. 1757.

Lion, Heyman. Treatise on Spinæ Pedum, 8vo. Edin. 1802.

Lipscomb, George. History of Canine Madness and Hydrophobia, 8vo. Lond. 1809.

Lister, Martin. Sex Exercitationes Medicinales De Morbis Chronicis, 8vo. Lond. 1694.

Lister M. De Fontibus Medicalibus Angliæ, 8vo. Lond. 1684.

Little, James. Essay on the Nature and Treatment of the Malignant Contagious Ulcer, as it appears in the British Navy, 8vo. Lond. 1809.

Lobb, Theophilus. Practice of Physic in general, 2 vols. 8vo. Lond. 1771.

Lobb, T. Rational Methods of Curing Fevers, the Effects of Bleeding, Vomiting, Purging, &c. 2 vols. 8vo. Lond.1785.

Lobb, T. Treatise on the Small-Pox, 8vo. Lond. 1741.

Locher, Maximil. Observationes Practicæ Circa Inoculationem Variolarum, 8vo. Vindob. 1768.

Locher, Maximil. Continuatio Experimentorum De Inoculatione Variolarum, 8vo. Vindob. 1769.

Lommius, Jodocus. Medicinal Observations, by Wynter, 12mo. Lond. 1747.

Lommius, Jodocus. Opera Medica, 12mo. Amst. 1745.

London Practice of Physic, 8vo. Dub. 1793.

Lossius, Fredericus. Observationum Medicinalium Libri quatuor, 12mo. Lond. 1672.

Lowe, Peter. Discourse of the whole Art of Chirurgerie, 4to. Lond. 1634.

Lucus, C. Method of Investigating the Properties of the Bath and Bristol Waters, 8vo. Lond. 1764.

Luxmore, Thomas. Familiar Observations on Ruptures, for the Use of both Sexes, 12mo. Lond. 1808.

Luxmore, Thomas. Practical Observations on Strictures of the Urethra, 8vo. Lond. 1809.

M

MACBRIDE, DAVID. Historical Account of a New Method of Treating the Scurvy at Sea, with Cases. Lond. 1767.

Macbride, David. Methodical Introduction to the Theory and Practice of Physic, 4to. Lond. 1772.

Mackenzie, James. History of Health, and the Art of Preserving it, 8vo. Lond. 1758.

Maclean, L. Enquiry into the Nature, Causes, and Cure of Hydrothorax, 8vo. Sud. 1810.

Maclean, Charles. Dissertation on the Source of Epidemic and Pestilential Diseases, 8vo. Lond. 1800.

Macquer, M. Elements of the Theory and Practice of Chemistry, 2 vols. 8vo. Lond. 1775.

Magatus, Cæsar. De Rara Medicatione Vulnerum, 2 tom. 4to. Lips. 1733.

Magenise, Daniel. Doctrine of Inflammation, founded on Reason and Experience, 8vo. Lond. 1768.

Maggius, Bartholum. De Vulnerum Curatione Tractatus a Gesnero, folio. Tigur. 1555.

Maiben, W. Treatise on the Use of Mercury, in certain Diseases, 8vo. Lond. 1809.

Makittrick, James. Commentaries on the Principles and Practice of Physic, 8vo. Lond. 1772.

Mandivelle, B. Treatise on Hypochondriack and Hysterick Diseases, 8vo. Lond. 1730.

Manning, Henry. On Female Diseases, 8vo. Lond. 1775.

Manning, Henry. Modern Improvements in the Practice of Physic, 8vo. Lond. 1780.

Manningham, Sir Richard. On the Nature, Causes, and Cure of the Febricula, 8vo. Lond. 1750.

Manningham, Rich. Equit. Aphorismata-Medica, Lond. 1756.

Marryat, Thomas. Therapeutics, or the Art of Healing Diseases, 12mo. Brist. 1805.

Martin, George. Medical and Philosophical Essays, on Various Subjects, 8vo. Lond. 1740.

Martinus, Georgius. De Similibus Animalibus et Animalium Colore, Lib. duo. Lond. 1740.

Maryan, William. Treatise on the Impossibility of the Disease termed Hydrophobia, being caused by the Bite of a Rabid Animal, 8vo. Lond. 1809.

Mathias, Andrew. Inquiry into the Nature and Cure of the Mercurial Disease, 8vo. Lond. 1810.

Mauriceau, Francis. On the Diseases of Women with Child, and in Child-bed, 8vo. Lond. 1683.

Maynwaring, Everard. Method and Means of Enjoying Health, Vigour, and Long Life, 12mo. Lond. 1683.

Mead, Richard. Whole Medical Works, 4to. Lond. 1768.

Mead, Richard. Medica Sacra, or an Account of Diseases mentioned in the Bible. Lond. 1762.

Mead, Richard. Discourse on the Plague, 4to. Lond. 1762.

Mead, R. Medical Precepts and Cautions, 4to. Lond. 1762.

Mead, R. Mechanical Account of Poisons, 4to. Lond. 1762.

Mease, J. Observations on the Inflammatory Nature of the Disease produced by the Bite of a Mad Dog, 8vo. Phil. 1801.

Medical Museum, or Repository of Cases, &c. 3 vols. 8vo. Lond. 1763-4.

Memoirs of the Medical Society of London, from 1787 to 1805 inclusive, 6 vols. 8vo. Lond. V. Y.

Memorial Concerning the Surgeons' Hospital of Edinburgh, 8vo. Edin. 1737.

Mercurialis Jerome. Consultationes et Responsa Medicinalia, 2 tom. folio. Venet. 1620.

Mercurialis Jerome. De Pestilentia et De Morbis Venenosis et Venenis, 4to. Venet. 1601.

Mercury, Crude, Remarks on the Danger of taking Internally, 8vo. Lond. 1733.

Merriman, Samuel. Dissertation on the Retroversion of the Womb, and Extra-uterine Gestation, 8vo. Lond. 1810.

Millar, Richard. Disquisitions in the History of Medicine, 8vo. Glas. 1811.

Millar, John. Observations on the Prevailing Diseases of Great Britain, 4to. Lond. 1770.

Millar, John. Observations on Asthma and Hooping-Cough, 8vo. Lond. 1769.

Millward, Edward. Letter on the Lives, Writings, and Characters of Medical Men, 8vo. Lond. 1740.

Milman, Sir Francis. Animadversions on the Nature, and on the Cure of Dropsies, by Swediaur, 8vo. Lond. 1786.

Mitchell. Medical Repository, 3 vols. 8vo. New York 1800.

Moffat, John. Translation of the Prognostics and Prorrhetics of Hippocrates, 8vo. Lond. 1788.

Moffat, John. Translation of the Eight Books of Aretæus on Acute and Chronic Diseases, 8vo. Lond. 1789.

Moises, Hugh. Treatise on the Blood, Animal Heat, &c. 8vo. Lond. 1801.

Monchy, Solomon De. Essay on the Causes and Cure of Diseases in Voyages to the West Indies, 8vo. Lond. 1762.

Monro, Alexander. Account of the Inoculation of Small-Pox in Scotland, 8vo. Edin. 1765.

Monro, Alexander. Description of all the Bursæ Mucosæ of the Human Body, fol. Edin. 1788.

Monro, Alexander. Observations Anotomical and Physiological, 8vo. Edin. 1758.

Monro, Alexander. State of Facts concerning Paracentesis of the Thorax, 8vo. Edin. 1770.

Monro, Alexander. Notes on the Postcript to a Pamphlet, &c. 8vo. Edin. 1758.

Monro, Alexander.   Answer to Notes on his Observations,
8vo.   Edin. 1758.

Monro, Alexander, Jun.   Morbid Anatomy of the Human
Gullet, Stomach, and Intestines, 8vo.   Edin. 1811.

Monro, Donald.   Observations on the Means of Preserving
the Health of Soldiers, 2 vols. 8vo.   Lond. 1780.

Monro, Donald.   Prælectiones Medicæ ex Cronii Instituto et
Oratio Aniversaria ex Harveii Instituto, 8vo. Lond. 1776.

Monro, Donald.   On Mineral Waters, 2 vols. 8vo. Lond. 1770.

Monro, John.   Remarks on Dr. Battie's Treatise on Madness, 8vo.   Lond. 1758.

Monro, George.   Account of the Treatment of Bilious Fevers
in the Military Hospitals of Martinico, 8vo. Lond. 1778.

Monro, Hugh.   Compendious System of the Theory and
Practice of Surgery, 8vo.   Lond. 1792.

Montanus, Johannes Baptist.   Consultationes de Variorum
Morborum Curationibus, 12mo.   Basil. 1557.

Monteath, Johannes.   Dissertatio Physiologica de Absorptione
Cutanea, 8vo.   Glas. 1808.

Moore, John.   Medical Sketches, 8vo.   Lond. 1786.

Moore, James.   Letter on the Composition of the Eau
Medicinale D'Husson, 12mo.   Lond. 1811.

Morgagni, John Baptist.   On the Seats and Causes of Diseases, by Alexander, 3 vols. 4to.   Lond. 1769.

Morley, John.   Essay on the Nature and Cure of Scrophu-
lous Disorders, 8vo.   Lond. 1773.

Morton, Rich.   Phthisiologia, or a Treatise on Consumptions,
8vo.   Lond. 1694.

Morton, Ricardus.   Exercitationes De Morbis Universalibus
Acutis, 8vo.   Lond. 1692.

Moseley, Benjamin.   Treatise on Tropical Diseases, and on
the Climate of the West Indies, 8vo.   Lond. 1803.

Moss, William.   Essay on the Management, Nursing, and
Diseases of Children, 8vo.   Egham. 1794.

Moy.   Rational Practice of Chirurgery, 12mo. Lond. 1686.

Moyle.   Chirurgus Marinus, or Sea Surgeon.   Lond. 1702.

Mudge, John.   Dissertation on the Inoculated Small-Pox,
12mo.   Lond. 1777.

Murphy, Joseph. Natural History of the Human Teeth, with a Treatise on their Diseases, 8vo. Lond. 1811.

Murray, John. Comparative View of the Huttonian and Neptunian Systems of Geology, 8vo. Edin. 1802.

Murray, John. System of Chemistry, with Appendix, 4 vols. 8vo. Edin. 1806.

Murray, J. Elements of Chemistry, 2 vols. 8vo. Edin. 1810.

Murray, John. System of Materia Medica and Pharmacy, 2 vols. 8vo. Edin. 1810.

Musgrave, Sam. Speculations and Conjectures on the Qualities of the Nerves, 8vo. Lond. 1776.

Musgrave, Sam. Gulstonian Lectures on Dyspnœa, Pleurisy, and Pulmonary Consumption, 8vo. Lond. 1779.

Musitanus, R. D. Carolus. Chirurgia Theoretico-Practica, 4 tom. 4to. Colon. 1698.

Musitanus, R. D. C. Opera Omnia Medica, fol. Genev. 1716.

N

NEALE, JOHN. On the Knowledge and Treatment of Gun-Shot Wounds, 8vo. Lond. 1805.

Neale, John. Essays and Remarks on that Species of Consumption, commonly called Tabes Dorsalis, 8vo. Lond. 1806.

Nevill, James. Description of the Venereal Gonorrhœa, showing the Ill Consequences of Purging, Injections, Astringents, &c. 8vo. Lond. 1754.

New Method for the Improvement of the Manufacture of Drugs, 8vo. Lond. 1767.

Newton, John Frank. Return to Nature, or Defence of Vegetable Regimen, 8vo. Lond. 1811.

Newton, Sir Isaac. Treatises on Reflections, Refractions, Inflections, and Colours of Light, 4to. Lond. 1704.

Nisbet, William. First Lines of the Theory and Pratice in Venereal Diseases, 8vo. Edin. 1787.

Nisbet, W. Concise View of the History, Nature, and Cure of Diseases, with a Practical Pharmacopœia, 12mo. Edin. 1796.

Nisbet, William. Concise View of the Nature and Treatment of such Diseases as form the Object of Surgery, with a Surgical Pharmacopœia, 12mo, Edin. 1799.

Nisbet, William. Concise View of the History and Treatment of such Diseases as form the Subject of Midwifery, with an Obstetrical Pharmacopœia, 12mo.   Lond. 1800.

Nisbet, William. Concise View of the Nature and Treatment of the Diseases Incident to Infancy and Childhood, with a Pharmacopœia, 12mo.   Lond. 1800.

Nisbet, William. Clinical Pharmacopœia, or the General Principles of Practice and Prescription, 12mo. Lond.1800.

Noble, Edward. Treatise on Ophthalmia, with New Methods of Cure, 8vo.   Birm. 1802.

Nooth, James. Observations on the Treatment of Scirrhous Tumours of the Breast, &c. 8vo.   Lond. 1806.

Northcote, William. Marine Practice of Physic and Surgery, 2 vols. 8vo.   Lond. 1770.

Nott, John. On the Influenza, as it prevailed at Bristol, in 1803, 8vo.   Brist. 1803.

Nuck, Anthony. Observationes et Experimenta Chirurgica, 12mo.   Lug. Bat. 1714.

O

Observations and Inquiries, Medical. By a Society of Physicians in London, 6 vols. 8vo.   Lond. V. Y.

Observations on the Effects of Sea-Water, in the Cure of Scurvy and Scrophula, 8vo.   Lond. 1770.

Okes, Thomas Verney. Account of the Spina Bifida, with Remarks on the Method of Treatment, 8vo. Lond. 1810.

Ontyd, C. G. Treatise on Mortal Diseases, 8vo. Lond. 1798.

Oribasius. Opera Chirurgica, a Gesnero, fol. Tigur. 1555.

P

Page, John. Receipts for Preparing the Principal Medicines of the late Mr. Ward, 8vo.   Lond. 1763.

Pallucci, M. Nouvelles Remarques sur la Lithotomie, 12mo.   Paris, 1750.

Paracelsus, Philip. Aur. Theoph. Chirurgia Magna, in duos Tomos Digesta, fol.   Argent. 1573.

Parey, Ambrose. Chirurgical Works, translated by Johnson, fol.   Lond. 1678.

Pargeter, William. Observations on Maniacal Disorders, 8vo. Reading, 1792.

Parkes, Samuel. Essay on the Utility of Chemistry to the Arts and Manufactures, 8vo. Lond. 1807.

Parkinson, James. Observations on the Act for Regulating Mad-Houses, 8vo. Lond. 1811.

Parr, Bartholomew. London Medical Dictionary, with Appendix and Plates, 3 vols. 4to. Lond. 1809.

Parson, James. Analogy between the Propagation of Plants and Animals, 8vo. Lond. 1752.

Patterson, William. Observations on the Climate of Ireland, 8vo. Dub. 1804.

Paulet, M. J. J. Histoire de la Petite Verole, 2 tom. 12mo. Paris, 1768.

Pearson, John. Practical Observations on Cancerous Complaints, 8vo. Lond. 1793.

Pearson, John. On the Effects of Various Articles in the Cure of Lues Venerea, with Cases, 8vo. Lond. 1807.

Pearson, John. Principles of Surgery, for the Use of Chirurgical Students, 8vo. Lond. 1810.

Pearson, Rich. Thesaurus Medicaminum, a Selection of Medical Formulæ, 8vo. Lond. 1810.

Pearson, George. Outlines of the Principles of Physic, 8vo. Lond. 1801.

Peachey, J. Introduction to the Art of Physic, Lond. 1697.

Peehlinus, J. N. De Purgantium Medicamentorum Facultatibus Exercitatio Nova, 8vo. Lug. Bat. 1672.

Pemberton, Henry. Course of Physiology, 8vo. Lond. 1773.

Pemberton, Henry. Dispensatory of the Royal College of Physicians in London, 8vo. Lond. 1746.

Percival, Thomas. Medical Ethics adapted to the Conduct of Physicians and Surgeons, 8vo. Lond. 1803.

Perfect, William. Annals of Insanity, containing Cases of Lunacy, Melancholy, or Madness, 8vo. Lond. ——.

Perry, Charles. Enquiry into the Nature and Principles of the Spaw-Waters, 8vo. Lond. 1734.

Perry, Charles. Account of the Hysteric Passion, and other Diseases Incident to the Sex, 8vo. Lond. 1755.

Perry, C.   Disquisitions of the Stone and Gravel, and other
Diseases of the Kidneys and Bladder, 8vo.   Lond. 1777.

Pestilence, An Inquiry into the Cause of, 8vo.   Edin. 1759.

Petit, J. L.   Treatise on the Diseases of the Bones, with
their Natures, Signs, Causes, and Cures, 8vo. Lond. 1726.

Pharmacopœia, Edinburgensis, 12mo.   Edin. 1735.

Pharmacopœia Collegii Regii Medicorum Edinburgensis,
12mo.   Edin. 1809.

Philalethes.   Treatise on the Plague, 8vo.   Lond. 1721.

Physic, Act for Establishing a School of, in Ireland. Dub. 1785.

Physicians, College of London, Animadversions on their
Legal Constitution, 8vo.   Lond. 1754.

Pigreus, Petrus.   Chirurgia cum aliis partibus Medicinæ,
juncta, 8vo.   Paris, 1609.

Pinckard, G.   Notes on the West Indies, and Respecting the
Seasoning, or Yellow Fever, 3 vols. 8vo.   Lond. 1806.

Pinel, P.   Nosographie Philosophique ou La Méthode, De
L'Analyse Appliquée a la Médicine, 2 tom. Paris, An.VI.

Pinel, P. Treatise on Insanity by Davis, 8vo. Sheffield. 1806.

Pitcairn, A.   Philosophical Elements of Physic, Lond. 1718.

Playfair, John.   Illustrations of the Huttonian Theory of the
Earth, 8vo.   Edin. 1802.

Plenck, Joseph James.   New and Easy Method of giving
Mercury in Syphilis, 8vo.   Lond. 1767.

Pomme, Peter.   Treatise on Hysterical and Hypochondriacal
Diseases, 8vo.   Lond. 1777.

Pott, Percival.   Observations on that Disorder of the Corner
of the Eye, called Fistula Lachrymalis, 8vo. Lond. 1758.

Pott, Percival.   Observations on the Fistula Lachrymalis,
8vo.   Edin. 1775.

Pott, Percival. Chirurgical Works, 3 vols. 8vo. Lond. 1779

Potter, T.   New and Complete System of Medical Practice
of the most Eminent Professors, 2 vols. 12mo. Lond. 1785.

Powell, Richard.   Translation of the London Pharmacopœia,
with Notes, 8vo.   Lond. 1809.

Power, George.   Attempt to Investigate the Causes of E-
gyptian Ophthalmia, 8vo.   Lond. 1803.

Priestley, Joseph.   Doctrine of Phlogiston Established and
that of the Composition of Water Refuted. Northum.1800.

Priestley, Joseph. Philosophical Empiricism, interspersed with Observations Relating to Different Kinds of Air, 8vo. Lond. 1775.

Priestley, J. History and Present State of Discoveries Relating to Vision, Light, and Colours, 2 vols. 4to. Lond. 1772.

Priestley, J. Directions for Impregnating Water with Fixed Air, 8vo. Lond. 1771.

Pringle, Sir John. Observations on the Diseases of the Army, 8vo. Lond. 1810.

Prior, Thomas. Authentic Narrative of the Success of Tar-Water, 8vo. Lond. 1746.

Profily, John. Easy and Exact Method of Curing the Venereal Disease, 8vo. Lond. 1748.

Purcell, John. Treatise on Vapours or Hysteric Fits, 8vo.

Purmannus, M. G. Newest and most Curious Operations in the whole Art of Surgery, by Cowper, fol. Lond. 1706.

Q

QUARIN, JOSEPHUS. De Curandis Febribus et Inflammationibus Commentatio, 8vo. Vien. 1781.

Quier, John. Letters to Dr. Monro, on the Small-Pox and Measles in the West Indies, 8vo. Lond. 1778.

Quier, John. Letters on the Bilious Colic called Dry Belly-Ache, 8vo. Lond. 1778.

Quincy, J. Complete English Dispensatory, 8vo. Lond. 1782.

R

RAMAZZINI, BERNARD. Opera Omnia Medica et Physiologica, 4to. Lond. 1718.

Ramazzini, Bernard. Practical Treatise on the Diseases to which Tradesmen are Liable, 8vo. Lond. 1705.

Ramsden, T. Observations on the Sclerocele, and other Morbid Enlargements of the Testicle, 8vo. Lond. 1811.

Ranby, John. Method of Treating Gun-Shot Wounds, 12mo. Lond. 1781.

Ranby, John. Narrative of the Last Illness of the Earl of Orford, 8vo. Lond. 1745.

Read, Dr. Whole Practice of Chirurgery, 8vo. Lond. 1685.

Reade, Joseph. Practical Observations on the Diseases of the Inner Corner of the Eye, 8vo. Lond. 1811.

Redmond, William. On the Principles and Constituence of Antimony, 8vo. Lond. 1762.

Rees, George. Treatise on the Primary Symptoms of Lues Venerea, 8vo. Lond. 1802.

Rees, George. Practical Observations on Disorders of the Stomach, 8vo. Lond. 1810.

Regnault, J. B. Essay on the Lichen Islandicus as an Aliment and Medicine in Consumption, 8vo. Lond. 1809.

Reid, Thomas. Essay on the Nature and Cure of the Phthisis Pulmonalis, 8vo. Lond. 1782.

Reid, Thomas. Directions for Warm and Cold Sea-Bathing, in Different Diseases, 8vo. Lond. 1795.

Reid, Peter. Letter on the Study of Medicine, and on the Medical Character, 8vo. Edin. 1809.

Reid, Henry. Essay on Ophthalmia, with Observations on its Causes, Symptoms, and Cure, 8vo. Portsea, 1806.

Reid, Thomas. Inquiry into the Human Mind on the Principles of Common Sense, 8vo. Glas. 1804.

Reid, John. Treatise on the Origin, Progress, Prevention, and Treatment of Consumption, 8vo. Lond. 1806.

Reide, T. D. View of the Diseases of the Army in Great Britain, America, and the West Indies, 8vo. Lond. 1793.

Report of the Committee appointed to Examine the Physicians respecting His Majesty's Illness, 8vo. Lond. 1789.

Report of the London Infirmary for Curing Diseases of the Eye, 8vo. Lond. 1810.

Review. The Medical and Chirurgical, from 1795 till 1807 inclusive, 15 vols. 8vo. Lond. V. Y.

Review, London Medical, from 1808 till 1811 inclusive, 4 vols. 8vo. Lond. V. Y.

Review of Mr. Aitken's Theory and Cure of Fevers, &c. 8vo.

Review and Magazine, the London Medical, from 1799 till 1803, 8 vols. 8vo. Lond. V. Y.

Review and Register, the Annual Medical, for 1809 and 1810, 2 vols. 8vo. Lond. V. Y.

Rhazes. Account of Small-Pox and Measles, by Mead, 4to. Lond. 1762.

Richerand, A. Elements of Physiology, by Kerrison, 8vo. Lond. 1807.

Richter, Aug. Gottlieb. Medical and Surgical Observations, 8vo. Edin. 1794.

Richter, Aug. Gottlieb. Treatise on the Extraction of the Cataract, 8vo. Lond. 1791.

Riddel, John. Remarks on the Nature, Causes, and Cure, of continued Fever, 8vo. Glas. 1788.

Rigby, Ed. Essay on the Uterine Hæmorrhage which precedes the Delivery of the full-grown Fœtus, 8vo. Lond. 1811.

Ring, John. Treatise on the Gout, and Observations on the Eau Medicinale, 8vo. Lond. 1811.

Riolanus, J. Guide to Physic and Chirurgery, fol. Lond. 1657.

Riverius, Lazarus. Practice of Physic, and Cases, with the Medical Counsels of Fernelius, folio. Lond. 1678.

Robert, M. Recherches sur la Petite Vérole et De L' Inoculation, 12mo. Paris, 1763.

Roberton, John. Practical Treatise on the Powers of Cantharides when Used Internally, 8vo. Edin. 1806.

Robertson, Archibald. Colloquia, Anatomica, Physiologica, et Chemica, 12mo. Edin. 1810.

Robertson, Robert. Obervations on Jail, Hospital, and Ship Fever in Europe and America, &c. 8vo. Lond 1789.

Robertson, Robert. Essay on Fevers, their Genera, Species, and Various Denominations, 8vo. Lond. 1790.

Robinson, Bryan. Treatise on the Animal Economy, &c. 8vo. Dub. 1733.

Robinson, Nicolas. Essay on Gout and Gouty Affections, 8vo. Lond. ———.

Robinson, Nicolas. New Method of Treating Consumptions, 8vo. Lond. 1727.

Robinson, Nicolas. System of the Spleen and Vapours, Low Spirits, &c. 8vo. Lond. 1729.

Rollo, John. Cases of Diabetes Mellitus and Lues Venerea, 8vo. Lond. 1798.

Rollo, J. Observations on the Diseases which appeared in the Army at St. Lucia, 1778 and 1779, 12mo. Lond. 1781.

Rosenstein, Nic. Ros. Von. On the Diseases of Children and their Remedies, 8vo.   Lond. 1776.

Ross, Johannes. Dissertatio Medica De Aliis Cerebri Injuriis, 8vo.   Glas. 1811.

Rowley, William. Cogent Reasons against Astringent Injections, Caustic Bougies, and Violent Salivations, &c. 8vo.   Lond. 1800.

Rowley, William. Essay on the Cure of the Gonorrhœa Virulenta without Internal Medicines, 8vo.   Lond. 1771.

Rowley, William. Essay on the Cure of Ulcerated Legs without rest, with Cases, 8vo.   Lond. 1771.

Royston, William. Observations on the Rise and Progress of the Medical Art in the British Empire, 8vo.   Lond. 1808.

Rulandus, Martin. Medicina Practica, 12mo. Franc. 1625.

Rules, Practical, for the Management and Medical Treatment of Negro Slaves, by a Planter, 8vo.   Lond. 1811.

Rumford, Benjamin Count. Philosophical Papers and Experiments, 8vo.   Lond. 1811.

Rumford, Benjamin. Count. Essays, Political, Economical, and Philosophical, 8vo. 3 vols.   Lond. 1800.

Rush, Benjamin. Medical Inquiries and Observations, 4 vols. 8vo.   Philadel. 1805.

Rush, Benjamin. Account of the State of the Body and Mind in Old Age, See Sinclair's Code.   Edin. 1807.

Rush, Dr. James. Inquiry into the Use of the Omentum, 8vo.   Philadel. 1809.

Russell, Ricard. De Tabe Glandulari sive De Usu aquæ Marinæ in Morbis Glandularum Dissertatio, 8vo. Lond. 1750.

Russell, James. Practical Essay on a certain Disease of the Bones termed Necrosis, 8vo.   Edin. 1799.

Russell, James. Treatise on Scrofula, 8vo.   Edin. 1808.

Rutty, John. Observations on the London and Edinburgh Dispensatories, 8vo.   Lond. 1776.

Ryan, Michael. Observations on the History and Cure of Asthma, 8vo.   Lond. 1793.

Rymer, James. On the Method of Treating Scrofula and other Glandular Affections, 8vo.   Lond. 1790.

Rymer, James. On Indigestion, Hypochondriasis, and Atonic Gout, 12mo.   Lond. 1786.

Rymer, James. On Dyspepsia, Hypochondriasis, and Gout, 12mo. Lond. 1795.

S

Saint-Yves, M. De. Nouveau Traité des Maladies des Yeux, 12mo. Paris, 1722.

Salmasius, Cl. Interpretatio Hippocratis Aphorismi LXIX. Sectione IV. De Calculo, 12mo. Lug. 1740.

Sanctus, Marianus. Tractati et Libelli Varii De Chirurgia, a Gesnero, folio. Tigur. 1555.

Sanctorius. Medicina Statica, or Rules of Health, in Eight Sections, 8vo. See Sinclair's Code. Edin. 1807.

Saporta, Anton. De Tumoribus Præter Naturam, Lib. v. 12mo. Lug. 1624.

Saumarez, Richard. New System of Physiology, 2 vols. 8vo. Lond. 1798.

Saunders, William. Observations on the Hepatitis of India, and Use of Mercury, 12mo. Lond. 1810.

Saunders, William. Treatise on the Structure, Economy, and Diseases of the Liver, 8vo. Lond. 1809.

Saunders, Robert. Observations on the Sore Throat and Fever in 1777, 8vo. Lond. 1778.

Saunders, James. Treatise on Pulmonary Consumption, and on Digitalis, 8vo. Edin. 1808.

Saunders, J. C. Treatise on some Particular Points Relating to the Diseases of the Eye, 8vo. Lond. 1811.

Saunders. New and Easy Method of Giving Mercury, 8vo. Lond. 1767.

Sauvages, Franc. Bois. De. Nosologia Methodica Sistens Morborum Classes, &c. 2 tom. 4to. Amst. 1768.

Scarpa, Antonio. Practical Observations on the Principal Diseases of the Eyes, by Briggs, 8vo. Lond. 1816.

Scarpa, Ant. Treatise on the Anatomy, Pathology, and Surgical Treatment of Aneurism, with Notes, by J. H. Wishart, 8vo. Edin. 1808.

Schomberg, Ralph. Treatise on the Colica Pictonum, or the Dry Belly-Ach, 8vo. Lond. 1764.

Scot, John. Inquiry into the Origin of the Gout, &c. 8vo. Lond. 1780.

Scultetus, Johannes. Chirurgion's Store-House, Illustrated with 40 Tables cut in Brass, 8vo.   Lond. 1674.

Senac, Jean. Treatise on the Nature and Treatment of Intermitting and Remitting Fevers, 8vo.   Philadel. 1805.

Sennertus, D. Institutions of the whole Arts both of Physic and Surgery, 8vo.   Lond. 1656.

Serny, J. B. Treatise on Local Inflammation, more particularly applied to Diseases of the Eye, 8vo.   Lond. 1809.

Sharpe, Samuel. Critical Enquiry into the Present State of Surgery, 8vo.   Lond. 1761.

Sharpe, Samuel. Treatise on the Operations of Surgery, 8vo.   Lond. 1782.

Shaw, P. New Practice of Physic, 2 vols. 8vo. Lond. 1726.

Shebbeare, John. Practice of Physic on the Principles of Physiology and Pathology, 2 vols. 8vo.   Lond. 1755.

Shebbeare, John. Candid Enquiry into the Merits of Dr. Cadogan's Dissertation on Gout, 8vo.   Lond. 1773.

Sheldrake, T. Practical Essay on the Club-foot and other Distortions, 8vo.   Lond. 1798.

Shirreff, Jacobus Hales. Disputatio Medica De Diabete Mellito, 8vo.   Edin. 1804.

Simmon, S. Foart. Observations on the Cure of Gonorrhœa, 12mo.   Lond. 1784.

Sims, James. Discourse on the Best Method of Prosecuting Medical Studies, 8vo.   Lond. 1774.

Sinclair, Sir John. Code of Health and Longevity, 4 vols. 8vo.   Edin. 1807.

Skelton, George. Practical Treatise on the Nature, History, and Cure of the Venereal Disease, 12mo.   Lond. 1808.

Smith, Hugh. Essays, Physiological and Practical, concerning the Blood, 12mo.   Lond. 1761.

Smith, J. S. Essay on the Causes of the Variety of Complexion and Figure in the Human Species, 8vo. Lond. 1789.

Smith, W. Dissertation upon the Nerves, 8vo. Lond. 1768.

Smyth, Carmichael. Description of the Jail Distemper amongst the Spanish Prisoners at Winchester, in 1780, 8vo.   Lond. 1803.

Spallanzani, Lazarus. Memoirs on Respiration, by Senebier, 8vo.   Lond. 1804.

Spallanzani, Lazarus. Dissertations Relative to the Natural History of Animals and Vegetables, 2 vols. 8vo. Lond. 1784.

Spectator, Medical, a Periodical Work, 8vo. Lond. 1792.

Spence, Georgius. Dissertatio Medica De Vasis Absorbentibus, 8vo. Edin. 1790.

Spon, Dr. Observations sur Les Fievres et Les Febrifuges, 12mo. Lyon, 1684.

Springell, Conrad. Translation of the Aphorisms of Hippocrates, and Sentences of Celsus, 8vo. Lond. 1735.

Springell, Conrad. *Natura Morborum Medicatrix*, or the Natural Cure of Diseases, folio. Lond. 1706.

Squirrell, R. Essay on Indigestion and its Consequences, with Remarks on Bathing, 8vo. Lond. ——.

Stedman, John. Physiological Essays and Observations on Pulses, &c. 8vo. Edin. 1769.

Steel, Franciscus. Dissertatio Medica De Inflammatione, 8vo. Glas. 1805.

Stempani, Holler. In Aphorismos Hippocratis Commentarii Septem, 8vo. Genev. 1677.

Stephen, John. Treatise on Consumptions, 8vo. Lond. 1761.

Stephenson, David. New Mechanical Practice of Physic, folio. Lond. 1745.

Sterne, Philip. Medical Advice on Disorders of the Lungs, 8vo. Lond. 1767.

Stevenson, William. Cases in Medicine, 8vo. Lond. 1781.

Stevenson, John. On the Morbid Sensibility of the Eye, and Weakness of Sight, 8vo. Lond. 1811.

Stewart, Dugald. Elements of the Philosophy of the Human Mind, 8vo. Lond. 1810.

Stewart, Alexander. Rules and Regulations for Preserving the Health of Seamen, 12mo. Lond. 1801.

Stock, Edmond. Medical Collections on the Effects of Cold as a Remedy in Certain Diseases, 8vo. Lond. 1805.

Stone, Arthur Daniel. Practical Treatise on the Diseases of the Stomach and Liver, 8vo. Lond. 1806.

Strang, John. Letters to a Student of Medicine on his Commencing Practice, with a Comparison of the Condition of Naval, Military, and Private, Practitioners, Lond. 1812.

Strictures on the Present Practice of Physic, Lond. 1778.

Struve, Christ. August. Asthenology, or the Art of Preserving Feeble Life, by Johnston, 8vo.   Lond. 1801.

Stuart, Alexander. Dissertatio De Structura et Motu Musculari, 4to.   Lond. 1738.

Stuart, Alexander. Three Lectures on Muscular Motion, read before the Royal Society, 4to.   Lond. 1739.

Surgeon, The Modern, or Plain and Rational Rules for the Direction of Practice, 8vo.   Lond. 1811.

Swediaur, F. Practical Observations on Venereal Complaints, 8vo.   Edin. 1793.

Swieten, Gerard. Baron Van. Commentaries on the Aphorisms of Boerhaave, 18 vols. 8vo.   Lond. 1759.

Sydenham, Thomas. Whole Works, Translated by Pechey, 8vo.   Lond. 1701.

Sylvester, Charles. Elementary Treatise on Chemistry, with the latest Discoveries, 8vo.   Lond. 1809.

Sylvius, De Le Boe Franciscus. Opera Medica Omnia, 4to.   Amst. 1679.

T

Tabes, Dorsalis, A Practical Essay on the Nature and Treatment of, 8vo.   Lond. 1748.

Tachenius, Otto. Tractatus De Morborum Principi, 12mo.   Osnab. 1679.

Tagultius, Joannes. Opera Chirurgica Omnia a Gesnero, folio.   Tigur. 1555.

Tar-Water, a Cure for the Epidemical Madness of Drinking, 8vo.   Lond. 1744.

Taube, William. Account of several Excellent Medicines Discovered from Argol or Tartar, 8vo.   Lond. 1757.

Taylor, Jean. Traite sur Les Maladies De L'organe immédiat De la Vûë, 8vo.   Paris, 1735.

Taylor, Thomas. Account of the Medical Properties of South American Bark, 8vo.   Lond. 1789.

Taylor, John. Account of the Mechanism of the Eye, and the Seat of Cataract, 8vo.   Norwich, 1747.

Temple, Sir W. Observations on Health and Long Life, 8vo. See Sinclair's Code   Edin. 1807.

Temple, Richard. Practice of Physic, or Concise Exposition of the Symptoms, Causes, and Cure of Diseases, with Formulæ, 8vo. Lond. 1798.

Templeman, Peter. Remarks and Observations on Medicine, Surgery, &c.; extracted from the Memoirs of the Royal Academy of Sciences at Paris, 2 vols. Lond. 1753.

Tennent, John. On the Epidemical Diseases of Virginia, particularly Pleurisy and Peripneumony, 8vo. Lond. 1742.

Thomas, Robert. Modern Practice of Physic, exhibiting the Causes, Symptoms, Dissections, and Cure of Diseases, 8vo. Lond. 1809.

Thomas, Robert. Medical Advice to the Inhabitants of Warm Climates, 8vo. Lond. 1790.

Thomas, William. Essay on Gonorrhœa, and the Use of Opium in the Cure of that Disease, 8vo. Lond. 1780.

Thomson, Thomas. Inquiry into the Origin, Nature, and Cure of the Small-Pox, 8vo. Lond. 1752.

Thomson, T. System of Chemistry, 4 vols. 8vo. Edin. 1802.
Same Book, Third Edition, 5 vols. 8vo.

Thomson, T. Elements of Chemistry, 8vo. Edin. 1810.

Thomson, Thomas. Historical, Critical, and Practical Treatise on Gout, 4to. Lond. 1740.

Thomson, Alex. Enquiry into the Nature, Causes, and Cure of Nervous Disorders, 8vo. Lond. 1782.

Thomson, John. Observation on Lithotomy, with Douglas' History of the Lateral Operation for Stone. Edin. 1808.

Thomson, A. T. Conspectus of the Pharmacopœias of London, Edinburgh, and Dublin, 12mo. Lond. 1810.

Thomson, A. T. London Dispensatory, 8vo. Lond. 1811.

Thorborn. Notes of Dr. Cullen's Lectures on the Practice of Physic, 7 vols. 4to. MSS.

Tissot, S. A. D. Advice to the People respecting Health, 2 vols. 12mo. Edin. 1766.

Tissot, S. A. D. Essay on Diseases Incidental to Literary and Sedentary Persons, 8vo. Dub. 1769.

Tissot, S. A. D. Lettre a M. De Haen, en response a ses Questions sur L'Inoculation, 12mo. Laus. 1765.

Tissot, S. A. D. Essay on Bilious Fevers, 8vo. Lond. 1760.

Tobacco-Plant, Observations on the Culture of, in Scotland,
8vo   Glas. 1782.
Tolet. Treatise of Lithotomy, or of the Extraction of the
Stone, by Lovell.   Lond. 1683.
Towne, Richard. Treatise on the Diseases most Frequent
in the West Indies, 8vo.   Lond. 1726.
Townsend, Joseph. Elements of Therapeutics, or a Guide
to Health, 8vo.   Lond. 1811.
Tracts, 8 French, respecting Inoculation and the Small-
Pox, 12mo.   Paris, V. Y.
Transactions, Medico-Chirurgical, by the Medical and Chirur-
gical Society of London, 2 vols. 8vo. Lond. 1809, and 1811.
Travers, Benjamin. Inquiry into the Process of Nature, in
Repairing Injuries of the Intestines, 8vo.   Lond. 1812.
Trotter, Thomas. View of the Nervous Temperament,
8vo.   Newcast. 1807.
Trotter, Thomas. Medicina Nautica, an Essay on the Dis-
eases of Seamen, 3 vols. 8vo.   Lond. 1804.
Trotter, Thomas. Observations on Scurvy, 8vo. Lond. 1792.
Trye, C. B. Essay on the Swelling of the Lower Extremi-
ties, incident to Lying-in Women, 8vo.   Lond. 1792.
Tulpius, Nic. Observationes Medicæ, 12mo.   Amst. 1685.
Tuomy, Martin. Treatise on the Principal Diseases of
Dublin, 8vo.   Dublin, 1810.
Turner, Daniel. Practical Dissertation on the Venereal Dis-
ease, 8vo.   Lond. 1727.
Turner, Daniel. Further Observations on the Venereal Dis-
ease, 8vo.   Lond. 1739.
Turner, Daniel. Art of Surgery, 2 vols. 8vo. Lond. 1736.
Turner, D. Treatise on Diseases of the Skin, 8vo. Lond. 1726.

U

Underword, Michael. Treatise on the Diseases of Chil-
dren, 12mo. 3 vols.   Lond. 1805.
Uvedale, C. On the Construction of the Nerves, and the
Causes and Cure of Nervous Disorders, 8vo. Lond. 1758.
Uwins, David. Modern Medicine, with Strictures on the
Present State of Medical Practice, 8vo.   Lond. 1808.

V

VALESCUS, DE T. De Medendis Omnibus, 4to. Franc. 1680.

Vander Linden, J. Anton. De Hemicrania Menstrua Historia et Consilium, &c. 4to. Lug. Bat. 1660.

Vander Linden, J. Anton. De Scriptis Medicis Libri Duo, 8vo. Amst. 1562.

Vauguion, M. De La. Complete Body of Chirurgical Operations, 8vo. Lond. 1716.

Venner, To. Via Recta ad Vitam Longam, a Plain Philosophical Demonstration, &c. 4to. Lond. 1637.

Verduc, Jean Baptist. Les Operations De La Chirurgie avec une Pathologie, 2 tom. 8vo. Paris, 1693.

Veslingi. Observationes Anatomicæ et Epistolæ Medicæ à Bartholino, 8vo. Hag. 1760.

Vetch, John. Account of the Egyptian Ophthalmia, &c. 8vo. Lond. 1807.

Vindication of the Managers of the Royal Infirmary of Edinburgh, 8vo. Edin. 1737.

Violante, Phillipus. De Variolis et Morbillis Tractatus Physico-Mechanicus, 4to. Drisd. 1750.

W

WADD, WILLIAM. Observations on the Best Mode of relieving Strictures of the Urethra, 8vo. Lond, 1811.

Wagstaffe, William. Letter on the Danger and Uncertainty of Inoculating for the Small-Pox, 8vo. Lond. 1722.

Walker, Richard. Memoirs of Medicine, including a Sketch of Medical History, 8vo. Lond. 1799.

Walker, Robert. Medical and Political Inquiry into Small-Pox, 8vo. Lond. 1790.

Walker, Sayer. Practical Treatise on Nervous Diseases, &c. 8vo. Lond. 1796.

Ward, Michael. On the Efficacy of Opiate Frictions in Spasmodic and Febrile Diseases, 8vo. Manchester, 1809.

Wardrop, James. Observations on Fungus Hæmatodes, or Soft Cancer, 8vo. Edin. 1809.

Wardrop, James. Essays on the Morbid Anatomy of the Human Eye, 8vo. Edin. 1808.

I

Ware, James. Remarks on the Purulent Ophthalmia which has lately been Epidemical in this Country, 8vo. Lond. 1808.

Ware, James. Observations on the Cataract and Gutta Serena, including a Translation of Wenzell's Treatise. on Cataract, &c. 2 vols. 8vo. Lond. 1812.

Warner, Ferdinand. Full and Plain Account of the Gout, 8vo. Lond. 1768.

Waterhouse, Benj. Cautions to Young Persons, concerning Health. See Sinclair's Code iv. Edin. 1807.

Watt, J. J. Encyclopedia of Medicine, Surgery, Midwifery, &c. 12mo. Lond. 1806.

Watt, J. J. Anatomio-Chirurgical Views of the Nose, Mouth, Larynx, and Faucis, folio. Lond. 1809.

Watt, Robert. Cases of Diabetes, Consumption, &c. with Observations, 8vo. Pais. 1808.

Watt, Giles. Dissertation on the Ancient and Noted Doctrine of Revulsion and Derivation, 8vo. Lond. 1754.

Webster. Facts Showing the Connection of the Stomach with Life, Disease, and Recovery, 8vo. Lond. 1793.

Wedelius, Georgius. Wolf. Amenitates Materiæ Medicæ, 4to. Jen. 1704.

Wells, W. C. Observations and Experiments on the Colour of the Blood, 4to. Lond. 1797.

Welsted, R. De Medicina Mentis Liber, 8vo. Lond. 1726.

Whately, Thomas. Description of an Affection of the Tibia, induced by Fever, 8vo. Lond. 1810.

Whately, Thomas. Cases of Extraordinary Polypi removed from the Nose, 8vo. Lond. 1805.

White, Charles. Narrative Respecting a Remarkable Operation on a Broken Arm, &c. 8vo. Lond. 1762.

White, Charles. Account of the Regular Gradation in Man, 4to. Lond. 1796.

White, William. Treatise on Inflammation and other Diseases of the Liver, 8vo. Bath, 1808.

White, William. Observations on the Nature and Cure of Phthisis Pulmonalis, 8vo. York, 1792.

White, Thomas. Treatise on the Struma or Scrophula, commonly called the Kings Evil, 8vo. Lond. 1787.

Whytt, Robert. Observations on the Nature and Cure of Nervous Diseases, 8vo. Edin. 1765.

Whytt, Robert. Review of the Controversy concerning the Sensibility and Moving Power of the Parts of Animals, 12mo. Edin. 1761.

Whytt, Robert. Observations on the Dropsy in the Brain, Experiments with Opium, Lime-Water, and the Remarkable Effects of Blisters, 8vo. Edin. 1768.

Whytt, Robert. Essay on the Virtues of Lime-Water in the Cure of Stone, 12mo. Edin. 1752.

Wilkes, Rich. Historical Essay on Dropsy, 8vo. Lond. 1777.

Wilkinson, C. H. Essays, Physiological and Philosophical, 8vo. Lond. 1798.

Willan, Robert. Reports of the Diseases of London, during the Years 1796, –97, –98, –99, and 1800. Lond. 1801.

Willich, A. T. M. Lectures on Diet and Regimen, and the Means of Preserving Health, 8vo. Lond. 1809.

Willis, Thomas. Five Dissertations on Urines, Blood, Muscles, Brain, and Nerves, folio. Lond. 1681.

Willis, Thomas. Essay on the Pathology of the Brain and Nerves, and Convulsive Diseases, Lond. 1681.

Willis, Thomas. Exercitations of the Operations of Medicines in Human Bodies, folio. Lond. 1678.

Willis, Thomas. Medical-Philosophical Discourse on the Various Kinds of Fevers, 8vo. Lond. 1678.

Willis, Thomas. Treatise on the History, Nature, and Treatment of Scurvy, folio. Lond. 1678.

Wilson, Andrew. Remarks on Autumnal Disorders of the Bowels, Bile, and Spasms, 8vo. Lond. 1765.

Wilson, Andrew. Inquiry into the Nature and Origin of Hysterics in the Female Constitution, 8vo. Lond. 1776.

Wilson, Alexander. Observations on the Influence of Climate on Vegetable and Animal Bodies, 8vo. Lond. 1780.

Wilson, Alexander P. Treatise on Febrile Diseases, 4 vols. 8vo. Lond. 1803.

Wilson, Alexander P. Essay on the Nature of Fever, and the Principles of its Treatment, 8vo. Worc. 1807.

Wirtzung, Christopher. General Practice of Physic, &c. folio. Lond. 1654.

Wiseman, Richard.   Chirurgical Treatises, folio. Lond. 1686.

Withers, Thomas.   Observations on Chronic Weakness, 8vo.   York, 1777.

Withers, Thomas.   Observations on the Use and Abuse of Medicine, 8vo.   Lond. 1775.

Wood and Monro.   Correspondence Respecting Stitching of the Intestines, &c. 8vo.   Edin. 1807.

Wood, Loftus.   Cases, Medical, Chirurgical, and Anatomical, with Observations, 8vo.   Lond. 1776.

Woodall, John.   Military and Domestique Surgery, and Treatise on the Plague, folio.   Lond. 1639.

Woodville, William.   History of Inoculation of Small-Pox in Great Britain, 8vo.   Lond. 1796.

Woodward, John.   Treatise on the State of Physick and of Diseases, 8vo.   Lond. 1718.

Woodward, John.   Cases and Consultations in Physic, 8vo.   Lond. 1757.

Wright, Thomas.   History of the Walcheren Remittent Fever, 8vo.   Lond. 1811.

Wurtz, Fel.   Experimental Treatise of Surgery, Lond. 1656.

Wylie, G. Dissertatio Medica De Enteritide, 8vo. Edin. 1810.

Wynter, John.   Essay on the Cure of Chronical Diseases, 8vo.   Lond. 1725.

Y

Young, Samuel.   Inquiry into the Nature and Action of Cancer, 8vo.   Lond. 1805.

Young, George.   Treatise on Opium, founded upon Practical Observations, 8vo.   Lond. 1753.

Z

Zimmerman, J. G.   Treatise on Experience in Physic, 2 vols. 8vo.   Lond. 1782.

BOOKS OMITTED.

Bonetus, Theophilus. Mercurius Compitalitius, Sive Index Medico-Practicus, &c. folio.   Genev. 1683.

Fracastorius, Hieronymus. Opera Philosophica et Medica Omnia, 2 tom. 8vo.   Lug. 1591.

Hunter, John. Treatise on the Natural History and Diseases of the Human Teeth, 4to.   Lond. 1778.

Hunter, John. Observations on Certain Parts of the Animal Economy, 4to.   Lond. 1786.

Lieutaud, Josephus. Synopsis Universæ Praxeos Medicinæ, 2 tom. 4to.   Paris, 1770.

Monro, Alexander. De Venis Lymphaticis Valvulosis et De Earum in Primis Origine, 8vo.   Edin. 1770.

₊ Besides the Books contained in the preceding Catalogue, the Subscribers have the use of ABOVE ONE THOUSAND THESES, including a great proportion of those which have been published in Edinburgh and Glasgow during the last Century, and many of the most important of those published on the Continent in the same Period. Manuscript Catalogues, arranged alphabetically according to the Authors' names and the subjects treated, may be seen at the Library, and will be printed as soon as the Collection is completed.—To increase this part of the Library, which is chiefly deficient in the last ten or fifteen years, Dr. W. will thankfully receive the contributions of his Friends.

Dr. W. has also made some progress in forming a MUSEUM for illustrating the different parts of the ANIMAL ECONOMY in Health and in Disease. Preparations or Specimens, which could tend to throw light on any of these Subjects, will also be gratefully received and acknowledged.

A LIST OF THE PAY OF THE MEDICAL DEPARTMENT OF THE ARMY.

	Full Pay per Day.	Nett Pay per Day.	Half Pay per Day.	Forage allowed if employed during Summer.	Expense of Commission.
Inspector of Hospitals,	2 0 0	1 15 0	1 0 0	19 0 0	12 12 6
Deputy ditto,	1 5 0	1 10 6	0 12 6	19 0 0	11 2 6
Deputy Inspector, after 20 Years Service,	1 10 0	1 6 3	0 15 0	19 0 0	11 2 6
Purveyor, for himself and Clerk,	1 5 0	1 1 10			
Deputy Purveyor,	0 10 0	0 8 9			
Physician,	1 0 0	0 17 6	0 6 0	19 0 0	11 2 6
Staff Surgeon,	0 15 0	0 13 1	0 6 0	14 5 0	10 12 6
Regimental Surgeon,	0 12 0	0 11 4	0 6 0	9 10 0	9 17 6
Ditto after 10 Years Service,	0 16 0	0 14 1	0 6 0		
Ditto after 20 Years Service,	1 2 0	0 18 10	0 6 0		
Surgeon of Militia,	0 12 0	0 11 4	0 6 0	9 10 0	9 7 6
District Surgeon and Apothecary,	0 10 0	0 8 9		9 10 0	9 7 6
Assistant Surgeon,	0 7 6	0 6 6	0 3 0	9 10 0	4 18 6
Hospital Mates,		0 6 6	0 2 0		

Regimental Surgeons retiring from ill health, contracted in the Service, after 20 Years, are to be allowed 10s. per Day; and after 30 Years, 15s. per Day.

Allowances are granted for Lodging-money and Travelling-expenses, at the following Rates:

Inspector of Hospitals, Deputy Inspector, Physician, and Purveyor, 1l. 1s. per Week Lodging-money, and 1s. 6d. per Mile Travelling-expenses.

Deputy Purveyor, Surgeon, and Apothecary, 15s. per Week, and 1s. 2d. per Mile.

Hospital Mate, 10s. 6d. per Week, and 9d. per Mile.

Purveyor's Clerk, 6s. per Week, and 9d. per Mile.

A LIST OF THE PAY OF THE MEDICAL DEPARTMENT OF THE NAVY.

	Full Pay per Day.			Half-Pay per Day.		
Physicians to the Fleet, - - - -	1	1	0	0	10	6
Ditto after three Years Service,	1	11	6	0	15	0
Ditto after ten Years Service, -	2	2	0	1	1	0
Physicians are allowed 1*l*. 1*s*. per Week Lodging-money when not provided.						
Surgeons of Hospitals or Hospital Ships, - - - - - - - - -	0	15	0	Same as		
Ditto ditto after ten Years, - -	1	0	0	Surgeons.		
Surgeons of Hospitals are allowed 15*s*. per Week Lodging-money when not provided.						
Dispensers of Hospitals, - - - -	0	10	0	0	5	0
Ditto ditto are allowed 12*s*. per Week Lodging-money when not provided.						
Surgeon, - - - - - - - - -	0	10	0	0	5	0
Ditto after six Years Service, -	0	11	0	0	6	0
Ditto after ten Years, - - - -	0	14	0	0	6	0
Ditto after twenty Years, - -	0	18	0	0	6	0
Hospital Mates, - - - - - - -	0	6	6			
Assistant Surgeon, - - - - - -	0	6	6			

Assistant Surgeons and Hospital Mates have no Half-Pay until they have served two Years, when they are entitled to 2*s*. per Day; and when they have served three Years. to 3*s*. per Day.

Assistant Surgeons who have not passed are paid no more than 5*s*. per Day.

The time as Assistant Surgeon or Hospital Mate is allowed in the Pay of a Surgeon, provided it does not exceed three Years.

Surgeons in Harbour-duty Ships (except Hospital Ships) are paid no more than 10*s*. per Day, however long they may have served, unless the Port Admiral's Flag is on board, as is sometimes the case, when they are paid the same as regular Surgeons.

Surgeons, &c. are allowed to retire, and receive the following pay:—after 20 Years, 6*s*. per Day; if from ill health, provided the Commissioners are satisfied that it arises from Service, 10*s*. per Day; after 30 Years, 15*s*. per Day.

PAY OF THE MEDICAL DEPARTMENT OF THE HONOURABLE EAST-INDIA COMPANY'S SERVICE.

	£ s.			Tons.
Surgeons, - -	5 0	} per Month, and	{	6 Privilege.
Assistant Surgeons,	3 10			3 Ditto.

This Privilege is allowed both Outward and Homeward, excepting in the Bengal Ships Homeward, when it is reduced to,

	Tons.
Surgeons, - - - -	4½
Assistant Surgeons, -	2¼

REGULATIONS
By the Faculty of Physicians and Surgeons of Glasgow,
Respecting Surgeons' Diplomas.

EVERY candidate for a Diploma must, previous to his being taken on trials, produce satisfactory evidence, that he has studied Medical Science *three complete Winter Sessions*, either at a University, or under resident members of the Colleges of Physicians or Surgeons of Edinburgh, London, or Dublin, or under members of the Faculty of Physicians and Surgeons of Glasgow; and that during that period he has attended public Lectures on the following subjects: namely, two Courses of Anatomy and Surgery delivered in different Sessions; one Course of Chemistry; one of Materia Medica; one on the Theory of Medicine; one on the Practice of Medicine; and one on Midwifery; and that he has attended one Year in a public Hospital, and studied practical Pharmacy in a regular Surgeon's or Apothecary's shop, during at least six months.

Candidates, who have served an apprenticeship of three or more years to a regular Practitioner, must produce evidence of their having attended all the above-mentioned Lectures, and a public Hospital, during the above-mentioned period; but the duration of their studies may be abridged to *two Winter Sessions.*

FEE.—FIVE GUINEAS.

J. Hedderwick & Co.
Printers.